x921
J455   CATALOG CARD COP 9
Wibberley,Leonard.
The gales of
spring.

3.25

DELANO			
SEP 6 '66			
AUG 5 '71	SO. BKSFLD.		
ARVIN MAR 3 '98			

★ The Gales of Spring ★

The Gales of Spring

Thomas Jefferson, the Years 1789-1801

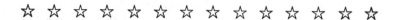

LEONARD WIBBERLEY

Ariel Books • *Farrar, Straus and Giroux* • *New York*

★ The Gales of Spring ★

☆ 1 ☆.

The winter of 1789 fell hard on the American continent, and the older folk declared that they had never known weather so severe. It was ushered in by violent October gales which delayed the shipping from Europe and caused heavy loss to many merchants in New York and Boston and Philadelphia. November brought blizzards of snow so that by Christmas the whole countryside as far south as Virginia was white and the snow continued on until April. It lay in drifts across the highways, tangling and impeding transportation. In the occasional thaws it plummeted in avalanches from the roofs of the houses of Boston and New York on the heads of the unfortunate citizens below, and small boys gained employment clearing snow off the roofs of the better houses to guard against such accidents.

The snow was great sport to the young folk but a great trial to their elders for there was little that could be done about it. Moved from the roofs, it blockaded the sidewalks. Moved from the sidewalks, it made the streets impassable to horse traffic. Moved from the streets in carts and deposited in New York in the Hudson and East Rivers, it was soon replaced by further snowfalls.

It was a trial which had to be borne, for it could not be coped with, and people longed for the spring though they grumbled that the thaw would bring floods such as few men had witnessed.

One citizen of the newly constituted United States of America was not unduly concerned by the heavy snowfall. Thomas Jefferson, Minister to France, had just returned to his homeland and arrived at Monticello, the lovely Virginia home of his own designing, on December 23, 1789. He had but one ambition, snow or no snow, and that was to rest for a while in his own house, enjoying the company of his family, his relatives and friends, free of all worries connected with government.

He would, of course, return to France for he was merely on a leave of absence from his post in Paris. Indeed, he had left the greater part of his baggage there. But now he had a little time for peace and quiet and private living, and he needed these things for he was tired and his estate had been neglected in his long absence abroad.

Jefferson had arrived in Norfolk, Virginia, on November 23, 1789, accompanied by his two daughters Martha and Mary, whose pet name was Polly. He stopped first to visit his sister, Mrs. Elizabeth Eppes at Eppington, where he received the first news that his plans to rest at Monticello and then return to Paris were likely to remain unfulfilled.

There were many letters waiting for him, among

them an envelope heavily sealed and addressed in a large bold hand which he knew to be that of George Washington. On the envelope was written "By Express," and Jefferson's heart sank when he received the letter for he knew that it had come by special courier which meant that it was an official rather than a friendly communication. He opened it and the smile of pleasure at being with his family left his face.

"What is it?" asked his sister. "Not bad news?"

"No," said Jefferson. "Not bad news. But heavy news. I had hoped to rest. I have been long away from home."

"And you cannot rest?"

"It is a matter of conscience," said Jefferson. "Can a man asked to serve his country refuse with a good conscience because he wishes to enjoy for a while the comforts of his own home? General Washington—President Washington—asks whether I will accept the post of Secretary of State in his cabinet. And I have not yet seen Monticello."

"You have a right to refuse," said his sister. "You have sacrificed too much of your private life already in the public cause." She was concerned about him for he looked suddenly old and worried.

"So has President Washington," said Jefferson. "More even than I. The last time I saw him happy, we talked together of improving the grass at Mount Vernon. Well, I shall have to reply quickly for he needs an answer soon."

That evening Jefferson wrote his reply. He told President Washington that he had hoped to return to Monticello, rest there a while and then return to France where, he hoped, the revolution would soon be successfully ended with a greater measure of liberty for the French people. Then he wanted to return to his home and withdraw completely from public life. These were his private hopes. But he would put them aside without any hesitation if Washington was convinced that Jefferson's services were essential for the success of his government. "It is not for an individual to choose his post," he wrote, and that was the key sentence of the letter.

The letter took Jefferson a long time to compose, but it was on its way by express rider to President Washington in New York by the following day.

Jefferson then went on to Monticello, there to be welcomed by his slaves who were so delighted to see the man who was their master that they uncoupled the horses of his carriage and pulled it themselves up the hill to Monticello. Then they lifted him out of the carriage and carried him in their arms up the steps and spent the rest of the night singing and dancing because he was back again. His daughter, Martha, was amazed at the devotion of the slaves who crowded to kiss his hands and embrace his knees.

Christmas was a happy one. The beautiful house was crowded with relatives and guests. The chandeliers glistened, the parquet floors were polished to the gloss of marble, there was music and dancing and laughter and lively talk, and Jefferson was able again to mount a hunter beautifully groomed and ride about his estates breathing the clean crisp Virginia air.

He did the things he loved to do, visiting every acre of his lands with his overseer, telling him to be sure to lay out hay for the deer in the parks or they would eat the bark of the trees, to see that there were turnips available for the cattle in their winter feed, and to give them some of the lucerne hay which was better fed to his own livestock than marketed, though the price was high. He visited his stables and his tackroom to satisfy himself that saddles and bridles were in top condition. He would not permit a bit to be used on a horse that was not polished to the sheen of silver, and he gave orders to the blacksmith to put heavier shoes on the hunters he would be riding now that the ground was frozen.

In France he had frequented the *salons* of the aristocrats, and had visited the homes of peasants and small farmers. He brought back a dozen ideas about farming that could be tried at Monticello. Two French sheepdogs were given to the overseer for use in guarding his own flocks, and the shepherd had to be taught the French words of command to which the dogs responded. It was a happy time but, like all happy times, tinged a little with sadness. For Monticello was the mansion which Thomas Jefferson had built with his wife Martha and she was dead now. Something of her still lingered about its rooms and hallways and left a loneliness which was to remain with him for the rest of his life.

The first Christmas at home in four years brought Tom Jefferson one great gift—a son-in-law. While in Paris, his elder daughter, Martha, had seen a great deal of her second cousin, Thomas Mann Randolph, of Tuckahoe, Virginia. He was the son of Colonel Thomas Mann Randolph, who had, in the early days, been a ward of Jefferson's father when his own father died.

★ 7 ★

The young man had been studying at Edinburgh and spent his vacations in Paris. There he had fallen in love with Martha, whom he had known since childhood. He asked Jefferson for his daughter's hand and Jefferson was delighted to give his blessing to the marriage. It meant a great deal to him. It meant the happiness of two young people of whom he was very fond, and it might also mean grandchildren. The two were married at Monticello on February 23, 1790.

During the Christmas holidays, one special friend visited Jefferson at Monticello—James Madison.

The two had not seen each other for several years. In that time when the Constitution of the United States had been drawn up, Jefferson had been in Paris and small, soft-spoken Madison had had the job of battling the Constitution through the Virginia Legislature to secure its acceptance. Virginia's ratification was essential, and aligned against Madison during the debate had been some of the greatest figures of the Revolution—Patrick Henry, James Monroe, Benjamin Harrison and George Mason among them.

None liked the Constitution which gave the Federal government too much power over their own legislatures, and Patrick Henry's blazing eloquence, calling on Virginia to reject the document, had nearly carried the issue.

But quiet James Madison, whose voice in debate never rose above the level of conversation, beat down the arguments of his opponents one by one. Point by point, he took every objection and answered it with quiet reason. In the end he won the legislature over, and Virginia voted for ratification. The Constitution was saved.

Jefferson himself had some qualms about the Constitution as it stood. "The best of governments tend eventually to tyranny," he told Madison. "We have set out the rights of the government and that had to be done. But equally we must set out the rights of the individual citizen which the government may never transgress. Man needs protection against his government and has inalienable rights which may never be taken from him."

" 'Nacheral rights'," said Madison in friendly imitation of the upcountry accent of Patrick Henry and they both smiled. "Nacheral rights," had been Henry's battle cry, one in which they had both joined and for which they had both fought, Jefferson more strongly than anyone in the old days.

"Yes," said Jefferson. "Natural rights. They must be spelled out, and not merely spelled out, but put down in a document as binding on the government as the Constitution. Otherwise we may have won nothing."

"It will be done, sir," said Madison. "All are agreed on it . . . the President, yourself, I, Henry . . . all." He paused. "All. All except a few."

"And the few?" asked Jefferson. "Come! Give me the news. No man knows the political situation better than yourself."

Little James Madison remained in deep thought for a moment. He was eight years Jefferson's junior and scarcely more than five feet six in height. He was slimly built and his hair was already receding so that he looked like a boy who, without quite achieving manhood, was growing old.

"You have heard of Mr. Hamilton?" he asked. "Our Secretary of the Treasury? He is a brilliant man, an ardent man, an honest man, and I think, a mistaken man."

"In what way mistaken?" asked Jefferson.

"He tends strongly towards what I will call the British point of view. He believes, unless I grossly misjudge him, that a monarchy is a good form of government. He believes that an aristocracy of people with wealth and land is a benefit to the nation, for such people, having much at stake, introduce a conservative and wise element into government which makes for the prosperity and stability of the country. He distrusts democracy. I find I put the matter too mildly. He *fears* democracy, thinking that people who are not possessed of title and land would, if given their way, produce a government without responsibility, one which would pass measures in the interests of the 'mob' that would ruin the nation. He believes our present Constitution an imperfect instrument which should eventually give way to one close to that of Britain."

"But Britain has no written constitution," said Jefferson.

"That is so," said Madison, "but he would model our Constitution on Britain's unwritten constitution— would establish perhaps a hereditary nobility among the wealthy men of the land, with an hereditary monarchy, which would provide the ruling class. The others—the mass of the people—are there only to be ruled."

Jefferson groaned. "That's the system we had in Virginia before we tore it down," he said. "George of England was the King and the tobacco planters the aristocrats. Aristocrats of wealth who handed their lands on to one son and were, by virtue of their wealth, the government of the whole colony."

"Mr. Hamilton would not find that so terrible a situation," said Madison. "He is at no pains to hide his view that a close liaison between government and property is essential. He believes that government should benefit the moneyed class and rule in their interests. The moneyed class, increasing in prosperity, would thus benefit government and the nation."

"And the President?" asked Jefferson.

"Hamilton is a brilliant man," said Madison. "He argues with fire and conviction. And he is Secretary of the Treasury. There is no one at present in the President's cabinet to give an opposing point of view."

Jefferson smiled. This was James Madison, all right. They had started to discuss the Constitution and Madison had contrived to bring the talk quite naturally to Jefferson's own appointment as Secretary of State. Not merely to the question of the appointment, but to the necessity of Jefferson's accepting it. However, Thomas Jefferson was not ready to capitulate.

"We fought this battle once before in the old House of Burgesses," he said. "The battles of the inherited wealth of the Tidewater planters and the rights of the ordinary people of Virginia."

"The tidewater, if I may express it so, is bigger now," said Madison. "It embraces the whole nation. That democracy which is now imparted in the Constitution of Virginia must be insured for the whole of the nation. The battle must be fought again."

But Jefferson still was not ready. "Tell me more of Mr. Hamilton," he said. "I have not had an opportunity yet of meeting him."

"His background?" asked Madison.

"If it is important. Nothing of gossip."

"Of course," said Madison. He paused. "The background in his case I think is important. He comes of obscure parentage—some hint at illegitimacy." He noticed a frown on Jefferson's face and hurried on. "This would not matter except that I think it has a bearing in this case. He was born on the British Island of St. Kitts in the West Indies and as a child, because of the obscurity surrounding his parentage, no doubt suffered the slights of society. These slights, I conjecture, drove him to work harder than children more favored in their parentage. He went to work early in some counting house and showed a marked aptitude for commerce and for writing."

"For writing?" asked Jefferson.

"Yes. Indeed, he wrote a description of a hurricane which struck the islands in such brilliant language that some of his friends banded together and got enough money to send him as an immigrant to this country to obtain an education. He went first to a grammar school in Elizabethtown, New Jersey and then to Kings College in New York. He studied probably harder than any student there, and when the Revolution broke out, joined our army and was soon, as you know, on General Washington's staff, as his secretary.

"He always wanted a field command but not being given one, quarrelled with General Washington and resigned to take up service in the field. I think he fancies himself a Caesar and though his great gift lies in commerce and in writing, he makes no effort to hide his conviction that he is a born soldier.

"His grasp of the principles governing commerce is remarkable and his choice as Secretary of the Treasury natural. I must add in all fairness that nobody worked harder to bring about the convention to ratify the Constitution than did Mr. Hamilton. But once the Convention met, he made but one address and then scarcely attended the meetings. Some kind of Constitution, he knew, had to be ratified. But he believes and says that our present Constitution must and will be changed in the direction of an aristocratic form of government. A Republic, for him, is but a step on the road to anarchy."

"And he is sincere in these beliefs?" asked Jefferson.

"Completely sincere, I assure you," said Madison. "He is utterly honest and completely dedicated to the good of the government as he visualizes the government. Frankness compels me to add that he is vain and ambitious to a fault. He is intolerant of contradiction or an opposing point of view, and he has yet to learn from experience the value of considering the opinions of others which run contrary to his own."

"Sir," said Jefferson, "I now find the reason, other than friendship, why you have favored me with this visit. I have had, since arriving at Monticello, a further letter from the President asking that I accept the position as Secretary of State. And I fancy no small part of your own journey here is to urge my acceptance."

"The President desires it. I desire it. The greater part of the people desire it. Your acceptance would bring great public comfort and joy," said Madison.

"And the extent of the office—what is implied in that title Secretary of State?"

"Not as heavy a burden as you may fear. Advice to the President on our foreign affairs and whatever may go with offering such advice. You will not find it overwhelming. I would be happy if I could return to New York with some hope that you will accept the post."

"I do not—I cannot—refuse it," said Jefferson soberly. To Madison it seemed that he spoke like a man accepting not a great honor but a great burden.

☆ 2 ☆

The Congress had long been a fugitive body, meeting
in semi-secrecy in remote places like Annapolis to
avoid the demands of soldiers, farmers and merchants
for payments of war debts. It had been a convention
of frantic men, trying to govern without the means of
government, trying indeed to establish a government
out of a victory that had caught the nation almost unprepared.

There was no treasury, there was no method of raising a revenue, there were no government officers and
there were no government departments. And even
had there been government departments there was no
money to pay the staffs or carry on the work of the administration. To be sure there was an army, but it had
dwindled to a mere symbol and there was no budget
for it. There was no navy because there was no
money for a navy. And until the Constitution was ratified and Washington elected President, no start could
be made on bringing the affairs of the new nation into
some sort of order.

Even the election of General Washington as the first President of the new country presented problems that seriously plagued the Congress which met now in New York. The office of President was utterly new so anything done in connection with it would set a precedent for all time. And there were many things, in view of this, which seemed important concerning the office of President of the United States of America. For instance: how was the President to be addressed? Some thought "Majesty" a fitting title and, curiously, many who wanted George Washington addressed as "His Majesty the President" were from Boston—the birthplace of the Revolution. Others felt "Excellency" sufficient, but the back country Senators and Representatives thought that all tomfoolery and said plain "Mister" was good enough.

And what about the Vice President? How was he to be styled? And where was the President to live and was the Vice President of almost equal standing with the President?

It was all confusing and it confused even so sound a man as Vice President John Adams until quiet James Madison pointed out that the Constitution had already given the President a title. It was simply, plainly, and beautifully, "President of the United States." That was good enough and the title remained.

But now General George Washington had become President George Washington, and Alexander Hamilton, working in a small room, was Secretary of the Treasury and big John Knox, who had surprisingly started life as a Boston bookseller, was Secretary of War, and John Randolph was Attorney General.

All that was needed to complete the executive

his branch of government was a Secretary of State and Thomas Jefferson was on his way from Monticello to New York to take up that post. There was no need for the Congress to avoid the people any more. It could meet openly in New York, though the Sergeant-at-Arms would not be called "Usher of the Black Rod" as Vice President John Adams, impressed by British Court procedure, had proposed.

The matter of the government indebtedness to its people would be handled by the competent Hamilton who could be trusted to find ways and means of raising a revenue. And Jefferson, wise and beloved, would see to it that the people's rights were not trampled down or the infant nation taken advantage of by some foreign power.

Business could be conducted then with confidence with such men in command, and already there were rumors around New York that the new government would pay every penny of its domestic war debt, down to the last penny of wages owed to the lowest soldier of the old Continental Army.

It took Thomas Jefferson a long time to get from Monticello to New York. He was delayed by the snows of that terrible winter that lasted into March. He left Monticello by the end of February but it was the twenty-first of March before he arrived. He was two weeks getting from Richmond, Virginia to New York City. At Alexandria an eighteen-inch snowfall bogged down his carriage, and he took to the public stage coach, sending his own carriage to New York by water.

He hitched one of his horses to the side of the stage coach so he could ride a little. At times the coach made only a mile in an hour. He heard that Benjamin

Franklin was ill in Philadelphia and interrupted his journey despite the vile weather to visit him. It was the last visit he was to have with Franklin, who had been something of a father to Thomas Jefferson and had comforted him during the nerve-wracking debate on the Declaration of Independence thirteen years before.

Franklin was very ill—dying, in fact. He had come down with a cold and, being a believer in fresh air, had insisted on throwing open the windows and breathing deeply the crisp air rendered frigid by the snows of that terrible winter. Now he had an inflammation of the lungs and knew that he would not leave his bed again.

But death did not concern him. He wanted only news of France, where he had been the Minister of the United States before Jefferson. What was really taking place there? Did Jefferson think the French monarchy would survive? What were the most recent proposals for a new form of government now that the revolution was in hand? What of Lafayette? What part was he playing? Emaciated by his illness, he fired question after question at Jefferson and seemed relieved when Jefferson expressed the belief that the revolution in France would be over in a year, and France would probably develop a constitutional monarchy such as existed in Britain.

That was a reasonable solution to the problem and Ben Franklin all his life had been a lover of reason. He could go now to his Maker in the belief that the future of his own country and that of France, which he loved too, was assured in liberty. He had lived a long long life and had seen a great growth of reason in the world, reason which had swept aside tyranny and privilege.

He gave Thomas Jefferson his blessing and watched with confidence as the tall Virginian walked out of his room and out of his life. They never met again, for two weeks later Benjamin Franklin was dead, slipping quietly, untroubled and unafraid, into eternity.

Jefferson arrived in New York to find a mountain of business awaiting him. There were baskets of communications, proposals, reports and questions all to be handled and all demanding instant attention. For staff he had five clerks, employed to make copies of correspondence. He did not know the extent of his own powers to make decisions and neither did anybody else. All that would have to be worked out. He found a small house to rent on Maiden Lane and plunged into his work. The revellers of the city, returning to their homes late at night, saw the gleam of candlelight from behind the curtains of Jefferson's study.

Jefferson had been to New York before leaving for France, but now he found the city much changed. It was bigger, its population swelled to thirty-five thousand people with more pouring in each month, so that the city was bursting at the seams—a condition which has continued to the present day.

Broadway, its principal thoroughfare, was paved for a mile from the Battery and beyond that deteriorated into an earth road which in the spring of 1790 was a wallow of mud. New roads were being built, tying up the bustling traffic of the city so that it was better to ride horseback or go on foot than attempt to get about in a carriage.

★ 19 ★

Gentlemen transported through the streets in Sedan chairs were frequently flung out as their bearers tumbled over holes in the roadway. Housing was unobtainable except at outrageous rentals. The shopping center lay at Nassau and William Streets which were crowded with the establishments of grocers and corset-makers, sword-makers, furniture upholsterers, ladies' tailors and gentlemen's tailors and makers of Peruke wigs which were then the fashion.

Not far from Federal Hall where the Congress met, auctioneers sold Negro slaves, knocking them down to the highest bidder. Gangs of slaves worked by night at the job of cleaning the city's necessary houses and dumping the contents into the river. The better houses had their own water wells and pumps, while others shared a common street pump, the servants carrying water to the kitchens in pails. The streets which contained these public pumps were always muddy from the slopping of the water. Hogs rooted in the gutters of all but the fashionable thoroughfares, and a country air was given to the place by the crowing of cocks at sunrise for it was advisable to keep a few hens, the price of eggs in New York being beyond all countenance.

These changes struck Jefferson, but what struck him more forcibly was the social climate of the city. He found developing around the person of Washington and also of Vice-President Adams a court circle with, to his eyes, all the marks of a royal court, and he was horrified.

When the President entertained formally at his home, he was seated on a couch elevated on a dias at one end of the room. All who entered were announced and walked to the couch where they made a bow, to which President Washington responded as best he could, sitting down, with a nod of his head. He shook hands with no one. His attitude was aloof and cold. And the women of the town pulled every string they could to be invited to these receptions and dressed with as much extravagance as Jefferson had seen at the court of King Louis at Versailles.

There was plenty of talk at social dinners of the benefits of a monarchical kind of government, with a nobility surrounding the court. Some argued with conviction that the Senate should be composed of American nobles, they should be appointed for life as members of the Senate, which would then be the equivalent of England's House of Lords.

Congressman Fisher Ames, who had ousted blunt Sam Adams as one of the representatives from Massachusetts, was of the opinion that democracy was, like death, "a dismal passport to a more wretched hereafter." Ames was a friend of Hamilton, who led the group that favored a monarchical form of government. But there were also others who distrusted democracy and looked for a change in the Constitution which would provide an American king and an American House of Lords. And all this amazed Jefferson who, at dinner party after dinner party, found himself the only democrat among the guests.

"I cannot describe the wonder and mortification with which the table conversations filled me," he wrote. "Politics was the chief topic and a preference of kingly, over republican, government was evidently the favorite sentiment."

Jefferson could not avoid getting into arguments

on this subject. Silence when the monarchists expressed their views might be taken as agreement, and so he had to speak out. Though he disliked personal arguments or any show of animosity, particularly when he was a guest at someone else's table, yet he found ways of squelching those who favored an aristocracy and who looked on Hamilton as their leader.

At one dinner where a guest held forth on the benefits of an hereditary monarchy, headed by a sovereign who was above party influence, Jefferson remarked quietly, but loud enough to be heard by the whole table, "I suppose there may be something to it. I have heard somewhere of a University where the Professorship of Mathematics was an hereditary post, passed on from father to son without any reference to their mathematical ability." There was a moment's silence and then a shout of laughter and the monarchists had been given something to think about without any individual being offended.

He was not long in New York before he met Hamilton for the first time and in the weeks immediately following his arrival had plenty of opportunity to watch Hamilton at work in meetings of the Cabinet.

Hamilton always managed to dominate these meetings. Thomas Jefferson did not at first resent this, for the matters under discussion were largely financial and so concerned the Treasury. He did not pretend to any deep knowledge of the financial problems of the new country, and they lay beyond the scope of his own department. He found Hamilton as Madison had described him—brilliant in argument, a master of all the facts relative to a particular case, and with an ability for understanding immediately the most complicated of problems.

He also found him charming and witty and strikingly handsome. And yet it disturbed him that Hamilton rather than Washington seemed at times to be conducting the cabinet meetings. It was Hamilton's agenda that was discussed and Hamilton's views that were expounded at length. There were times when Jefferson caught himself wondering whether Hamilton did not consider himself at least the equal of all those present, including George Washington himself.

The brilliant New York drawing rooms might be concerned with forms of government but the Congress in Federal Hall was concerned with money. It was concerned with money in the form of the debts which the nation owed to farmers and merchants, soldiers and sailors. Hamilton had proposed in a "Report on the Public Credit" which was submitted to the Congress that the United States discharge its debts in full. It was an honorable proposal and the report was heard in the Senate in secret and behind locked doors. But in the House of Representatives the secrecy was hardly complete. The galleries were filled with speculators who saw in a statement by the Secretary of the Treasury an excellent chance for profit.

Hamilton's recommendation, when fully presented, was that the Federal Government should not only pay all debts contracted by the Continental Congress but should also pay off in full all the debts contracted by the separate States during the war. This taking over of state debts was called "Assumption," and the proposal was loudly praised by some and loudly damned by others.

Why should Vermont pay off the war debts of Virginia, and North Carolina be responsible for the public debts of New York? Some states had only small debts and others large ones. Was it fair then that all should carry the same load? That was one argument.

Others distrusted the whole business of the Federal Government assuming payment of state debts. Certainly it was nice for a state to have its financial burden eased in such a manner. But wasn't there here also a strong hint of surrender of state finance to the national government? Wouldn't such a precedent make the states dependent on the national government in financial matters? Money was power and, if the power of money lay with the Federal Government, then the state governments would soon be trodden underfoot.

Others looked askance at Hamilton's proposal that the government should be forbidden to pay more than two percent of the principal sum of the debts each year. What was the meaning of such a provision, they asked? The debt couldn't be paid off at that rate for fifty years, and the interest on it would run far higher than the debt.

Hamilton replied that a long period of payment was proposed because there were other needs for public money beyond the payment of war debts. It would be short-sighted to let the debt levy a bigger demand on the treasury. But many argued that Hamilton was merely providing out of the public treasury a source of income for fifty years for those who held certificates of indebtedness.

And then it began to dawn on many people that the soldiers of the Revolution no longer held these certificates, which had been given them at the end of their service, certifying that they were owed such and such a sum of money.

There were hundreds and thousands of such certificates given the discharged men of the Continental Army. And the men had had to part with them far below their face value. Some had sold their certificates for two shillings in the pound—one-tenth of the face value. Speculators had bought these certificates up. These speculators then, who had not perhaps heard a shot fired in anger, were to collect the soldier's wages, with interest, over a period of fifty years? And who was to pay this money? Why, the soldiers themselves, for the taxes to provide payment would come out of their pockets. They had sold their inheritance for a bowl of porridge and would now be called upon to pay the full price of the inheritance—with interest.

Indeed, before Hamilton had submitted his report on the public credit to the Congress, news of what it contained had leaked out. Horsemen were sent into the back country of every state, buying up the soldiers' script as well as that of farmers at a tremendous discount. The traffic even reached the extent of one member of the Congress sending a ship to the southern states, with agents aboard to buy up all the script they could lay hands on.

By land and by sea then, the couriers went into the countryside buying up the certificates, and Jefferson was horrified to discover that many members of the Congress who would vote on Hamilton's proposal were themselves speculating in script.

All this debate on what was called "Assumption" took place before Jefferson reached New York to take up his post as Secretary of State. He knew little of it and did not meddle in it. It was left to his friend, James Madison, to lead the attack on Hamilton's plan and bring into the open, in congressional debate, the whole sordid business of the fortunes that were being made by speculators buying up the script of soldiers. The papers of the day, of course, had their say on the subject. But Madison spoke officially as a representative from Virginia.

He never for a moment denied the need for the nation to pay off the war debts and assume the war debts of the different states. He spoke earnestly and convincingly in favor of this part of Hamilton's plan. But he said the debt was, in all justice, owed to the soldiers and the merchants who had been of service to their country in its time of crisis, and not to the speculators who had bought up their certificates.

To be sure, the speculators had risked their money in buying certificates that might be worthless. But they now stood in a fair way to make a huge profit while those who had served their country would suffer a tremendous loss.

The way to do justice to both parties, Madison said, was to pay the original holder of the certificate in full. If the original holder had assigned his certificate to someone else, then that second party should be paid the highest current market value of the certificate and the original holder should get what remained.

Madison's proposal raised a terrible storm. Some cheered him as the champion of the common man and the ex-soldier. Others denounced him a wild dreamer who would wreck the nation's credit. How could his plan be put into operation? How would it be possible to trace the original owner of a certificate which might have passed through a dozen hands by this time? Madison himself knew that his plan would be difficult to put into operation; when the House met to consider it, it was voted down.

Then Hamilton, having marshalled all his forces in the Congress, had the matter of the "Assumption" of state debts brought to a vote. It failed to pass by two votes and the whole plan which, whatever its drawbacks, was intended to establish the public credit of the government, was tumbled into ruin.

It was after this defeat that Jefferson arrived in New York, and Hamilton, searching desperately for means to get the Congress to reverse itself, decided to try to enlist the help of the new Secretary of State. Jefferson, though no meddler in politics, carried immense influence throughout the nation and particularly with many members of the Congress. Hamilton had done what he could to secure more Congressional support for Assumption. He had tried a trade, offering in return for votes, his influence in having the national capital located in the state of those who would support his scheme.

He might win over some Virginian votes by promising to do his best to have the national capital located in Virginia, perhaps at Georgetown, or get Maryland votes with a promise to work for the establishment of the capital in Baltimore. He canvassed the representatives of the different states—Virginia, Maryland, Pennsylvania—hinting at the prospect of being able to have the national capital located in their states in return, of course, for votes. And still, he was not sure of victory. He needed one vote in the Senate and five in the House for passage of his measure. He could not be certain of them. He decided then to seek the support of the new Secretary of State, Thomas Jefferson, for his measure.

The two had known each other at this point for only three months. They were on friendly terms, each working away at the business of his own department. No rivalry had developed between them. And so, one June morning, when Jefferson was on his way to visit President Washington, with whom he had some business, Hamilton stopped him in the street.

"Sir," he said, taking Jefferson by the arm. "Give me a few moments of your time, I beg you."

"Certainly," said Jefferson, surprised that Hamilton should seem so distracted.

"I have a grave matter to discuss on which I need your help," said Hamilton. "The whole future of the nation, I believe, rests on the issue."

"Shall we go to some suitable place to talk?" asked Jefferson.

"No," said Hamilton. "Let me explain the situation here now." And so, walking side by side up and down before the President's house, Hamilton poured out to Jefferson the whole story of his Assumption plan. Jefferson knew the details but Hamilton put them in a dramatic light for him. The issue, he said, was whether the nation should exist unified or whether the states should all go their separate ways and the Revolution then be lost. The public credit had to be established. The national government had to take over and discharge the debts of the states.

"You hardly need me to tell you, sir," said Hamilton, "that the recent war was fought not by thirteen separate states but by a nation which consisted of the union of those thirteen separate states. The struggle was a common one for a common liberty and it cannot be pretended that the muskets paid for by New York did not benefit the people of Georgia.

"Yet the southern states oppose my plan, claiming that their debts are not as great as those of the northern and eastern states. Though united in the conflict we are now falling out, and our union threatened over a squabble about who shall pay the bill."

Jefferson listened intently while Hamilton poured out the story. Hamilton made no secret of the fact that some southern votes could be won if the national capital were established in a southern state. There was the possibility of a trade—a trade which was necessary to save the credit and the unity of the new nation.

There were some points on which Jefferson was not satisfied. Was it possible to establish the exact amount of each state's war debts? Was it possible to sift out expenditures by each state which were not necessarily connected with the war? Again, presumably the national government would settle the matter by paying to each state government the amount of its indebtedness, and the state governments then would reimburse the individual payments. But what was to prevent some states from profiteering out of this procedure, grabbing public funds to hand out and enrich their citizens? All these points concerned Jefferson, for he well knew that money spelled political power.

Hamilton could not give him too much assurance on these questions. But he said that though there would be some abuses, nevertheless the main danger to avoid was the splitting up of the Union. Some of the northern states were threatening to withdraw from the Union and go their separate ways. This prospect appalled Jefferson.

"Dine with me tomorrow, Mr. Hamilton," he said. "I will bring together one or two people who can talk the matter over privately. Perhaps we shall find some solution."

"If we find a solution, Mr. Jefferson," said the other, "we will have saved our country." He left then and Jefferson climbed the steps to Washington's residence in deep thought.

It was strange indeed that Hamilton had spoken to him in the street on such an important matter. Was it out of sheer desperation and anxiety? Or was there some other reason?

Jefferson brushed the thought aside and went in to see the President.

☆ 3 ☆

The dinner to discuss the question of Assumption was held in Thomas Jefferson's house on Broadway and present, beside himself, were Alexander Hamilton and two members of the Virginia delegation to Congress, Richard Bland Lee and Alexander White.

They were neither of them eminent men in the sense that Madison was an eminent man. But they were solidly representative of that sentiment in the southern section of Congress which opposed the national assumption of the state debts and which also wanted the national capital to be situated in one of the southern states.

The dinner was good, without being lavish. The menu had a French touch to it in the serving of hors d'oeuvres and a light table wine with dinner, for Jefferson was fond of French cuisine and planned to import his old chef from Paris. The talk during dinner, while the servants tended the table, was of the social affairs of the city—a reception at the fashionable Mrs. Bingham's house, the health of Mrs. Randolph, wife of the Attorney General, whose illness had been the cause of her husband's absence from the cabinet, and scarcity of cherries on the New York market, due perhaps to the severity of the winter.

It was only when the cloth was cleared and the servants had retired that the talk got around to the matter of assumption of state debts. Jefferson, as host, acted as chairman but took no part in the discussion other than to guide it in directions he thought fruitful. He did not feel qualified to talk on financial matters, though he was concerned over the threat to the unity of the country.

"We cannot," he said, "have the nation divided between north and south whatever the issue. Differences of opinion there will always be. But complete division, each opposing the other, will but tear the country apart."

He turned with a slight smile to Lee, "I would remind you, sir," he said, "that it was our own Patrick Henry of Virginia who first said, 'I am not a Virginian. I am an American.' It is in the spirit of being American that we must consider all our national problems."

"True, sir," said Lee, "but there is nothing to prevent a man being a Virginian as well as an American. And there is little doubt in our minds that the eastern and northern states are working against us to obtain advantages at our expense. In this matter of the assumption, the greater part of the money, if the measure is carried, would go to the eastern states and we would pay for it. And yet it was these same states that defeated our bid to have the national capital in the south. They want their bread buttered on both sides and demand to boot that we supply the butter."

"I think you misunderstand the sentiment, Mr. Lee," said Hamilton. "The eastern or northern states, whichever you want to call them, are not adamant against the capital being in the southern section. They are prepared, I believe, to give a little there."

"For a price no doubt," said White.

"Everything has its price," said Hamilton. "It would be childish to pretend that that is not so. It is the part of grown men to consider prices and whether it is to their advantage to pay them."

The talk went on and out of it came a compromise. If the northern members of Congress would agree to the site of the nation's capital being in the South, enough of the southern congressmen would change their votes to assure passage of the assumption measure.

"I'll tell you frankly," said Alexander White when the discussion closed, "I'll change my vote, but I will have to hold on to my stomach while I do it, Mr. Hamilton."

"There are some measures of national interest which demand that a man have a strong stomach," replied Hamilton smoothly.

And so it was arranged. What came out of Thomas Jefferson's supper was the saving of the national credit and the birth of Washington, D. C. on ten square miles of territory which if it was not southern, was not northern either.

Later, when he thought this compromise over, Thomas Jefferson was not so sure that he had acted wisely. He complained to Madison that he had been duped by Hamilton, who had overstated the situation, pretending that a crisis existed over assumption which would tear the Union apart though this was not by any means true. He began to distrust Hamilton.

That curious conference in the street which Hamilton had insisted on puzzled him. And then Jefferson decided the conference had been held in the street for the purpose of propaganda. The whole town, which lived on its own political gossip, would know of the meeting in a matter of hours, and southern congressmen, who looked to Jefferson as a natural leader, would assume he was cooperating with Hamilton. That would soften some of their opposition to the plans of the Secretary of the Treasury. Watching Hamilton at work in the cabinet, dominating the meetings, pleading for powers which, in Jefferson's belief, would benefit the business section of the nation at the expense of the ordinary man, Jefferson wondered whether Hamilton's politics would insure the kind of liberty for Americans that Jefferson wished them to have.

Hamilton made no pretense of favoring a complete democracy. The mass of people were not to be trusted with government. That was his view. Government should seek a close liaison with business and pass such laws as would benefit the business community. The business community would then support the government, making for a stable institution not readily to be overthrown by popular emotion. As Jefferson listened to Hamilton in the cabinet meetings, he began to see this all the more clearly.

"He believes in the power of the purse rather than the power of the people," he remarked to a friend. "That can lead to corruption."

"You think Mr. Hamilton corrupt?" he was asked.

"Not at all," cried Jefferson. "I believe him as honest and incorruptible a man as may be found. Yet his policies, if pursued, must one day bring a confrontation between profit and patriotism. Tell me, sir, how many men do you know who would pass up the opportunity of turning a profit of several thousands of dollars for patriotic reasons? In a contest between profit and patriotism, patriotism is likely to come off second best. He who stands to make the profit will not lack for arguments to convince himself that to do so is in the country's best interests."

"But surely, Mr. Jefferson, you will agree that the general prosperity of the nation produces the good of the nation; that if our businesses flourish then our finances are sound and our nation benefits therefrom?"

"The general prosperity of the nation," replied Jefferson, "is as likely to be promoted by a lone man clearing a portion of the wilderness to turn into a farm as by the opening of a new smelting works in Massachusetts. Admitting the importance of the opening of such works, what measures has Mr. Hamilton in mind to help the pioneer on our western frontiers, or the small farmer anywhere in the nation? None, sir. He can see business but he cannot see the whole community. He can trust commerce but he cannot trust the people. It is with the people and their liberties and prosperity that I am concerned."

And there it was—a division of views between the two leading members of President Washington's cabinet which could not be reconciled but came to the fore in every meeting of the cabinet. The division grew worse as summer slipped into autumn. Hamilton favored an aristocracy, indeed, in Jefferson's view, a monarchy. He had wide support in the cities among the wealthy men of commerce and business. Jefferson favored a democracy on the largest basis. The whole of New York appeared to be in Hamilton's camp, and although on his first arrival in the city, Jefferson had been invited to dinner after dinner, and one social occasion after another, his contempt for a government of privilege, which he was not at pains to hide, made him less and less popular.

He began to find himself left out and lonely. The slight of personal friends hurt him. His deep fear that public liberty was being pawned for private profit weighed heavily on his mind. He suffered severe headaches which lasted three or four days, never letting up day or night. He lost weight and sleep and began to dread the cabinet meeting where, as he told Madison, he and Hamilton were pitted one against the other like fighting cocks in a pit.

The leaning towards a monarchy which Jefferson found in the *salons* of New York, particularly among the supporters of Hamilton, troubled Jefferson as deeply as any other matter. There were times when he wondered whether Washington himself was not, by the ceremony that attended the President's official appearances, unwittingly giving support to those who would like to see an American king.

This ceremony appalled Jefferson. He was horrified to see the President and his wife sitting on a sofa at one end of a reception room as if on a throne while all who entered bowed to him. He noted that on official occasions Washington never shook hands with any one. At his own levees or official visiting periods, he always stood and his aspect was aloof and even cold.

His coach was ornate and attended by outriders and wherever he went there was a buzz of "Excellency" that to Jefferson's ears began to sound like "Majesty."

When he attended the theatre, Washington was met by an usher at the door and led to what, to Jefferson, appeared to be a royal box with the coat of arms of the United States on the front of it. Soldiers were posted at the doors of the theatre when the President attended, and if he were late, the performance did not start until he was seated. A republic? It looked to Jefferson more like a monarchy.

Jefferson was not a man to hide his feelings on this matter and several times he spoke to Washington about the impression he was creating. "It begins to look as though you are intent on establishing a court, like that of a king," Jefferson said. "The people ape what they see you tolerate. Why, there are social occasions around the town that look like entertainments of the French aristocracy—precedent given to people in their seating at a table as if we already had among us Earls, Dukes, Counts and Knights. The other evening there was a dance, if you please, at a certain house where the gentlemen were requested to appear in swords. And those who did not wear a court sword were not admitted."

"What am I to do?" asked Washington. "The people wish to pay some kind of tribute to the office of President. I assure you it is no comfort to me to be sitting on that confounded sofa being bowed to here and there all evening. Why, sir, if I do not make the correct kind of nod in return I get complaints from people who were my friends. My nod was too cold. My nod was too aloof. Great Heavens! Doesn't it occur to any of them that my nod might be the result of a stiff neck from sitting there through several hours of discomfort when I would as soon be at my own fireside? And, in all this abundance of nodding, if I miss nodding to one, I have made an enemy for life."

"That is precisely the point," said Jefferson. "Do away with it all and none will be offended by missing a nod."

"The people have a right to show their respect to the office of President of the United States," replied Washington. "It is my duty to respect their desires and endure whatever personal discomfort may be involved. As for your fears of a monarchy, I do not have to tell you that such a concept is utterly repugnant to me."

"Of that I am entirely aware," said Jefferson.

"I have not helped defeat George the Third of England to become George the First of the United States," said Washington. For all his monumental patience, there were times when Washington lost his temper and he was close to doing so now.

"I had no such thoughts," said Jefferson. "I hardly think that I deserve even the suggestion of a rebuke."

They parted. But on several other occasions Jefferson returned to the topic of the adulation and ceremony that was heaped on the President who felt that he must endure it because of his office. Washington's view was that with the passage of time the court atmosphere that surrounded him against his will would dwindle. Jefferson's was that it would not dwindle but increase, and fan the hopes of those, headed by Hamilton, who would see a king and a nobility established in the United States.

Even wise John Adams, as staunch a republican as there had ever been before the Revolution, seemed now hypnotized by the glitter of pomp and ceremony. He had been appointed, before becoming Washington's Vice-President, American Minister of the Court of St. James—to the court then, of King George III. The king had received him graciously and Adams, watching the operation of the British system, had been greatly impressed by it. It contained a built-in order and a mutual dependence, one class on the other, that appealed to him. Above all, commanding the respect and the loyalty of all, was the king. Below him were the lords, bound to their king by mutual interest and long association of their families with his family or at least the throne. Below these were the commons, also bound to the king by generations of service to the throne in which they delighted—and also respectful of the lords who, to retain that respect, generally preserved the rights of the commons.

The system had become corrupt through long usage. But stripped of its corruption, it was excellent and some proof of its excellence lay, in John Adams' mind, in the fact that the king's first minister was often a commoner.

Once, at dinner with both Hamilton and Jefferson, when the talk had turned, as it so often did, to the form which governments should take, Adams described and praised the British system.

"Purge that Constitution of its corruption and give to its popular branch equality of representation and it would be the most perfect constitution ever devised by the wit of man," said Adams.

There was a slight pause and then Hamilton spoke

up. "Purge it of its corruption and give to its popular branch equality of representation and it would become an impracticable government," he said. "As it stands at present, with all its supposed defects, it is the most perfect government that ever existed."

Jefferson was astounded. Did this mean that Hamilton was not only a monarchist but also a monarchist who favored corruption in government? The more he thought of the matter, the more he decided that this was so.

Hamilton, whose own character was beyond reproach, seemingly regarded corruption as a necessary part of government and thus no great evil.

☆ 4 ☆

During his first months in office as Secretary of State, Jefferson kept in close touch, by letter, with his family and his friends. His heart was always in Monticello and amid all the cares of his office, he turned constantly to his home for strength to keep going. He delighted in discussion and debate but hated dissension and discord which served no useful purpose but merely inflamed the issue and brought on emnity and suffering. And so, from the heated political atmosphere of New York, he turned to his daughters in Monticello for news of their doings and how his estates were faring.

His elder daughter Martha, nicknamed Patsy, was seventeen. She was now Mrs. Thomas Mann Randolph but lived at Monticello with her husband and she was a good correspondent. Martha, though but a child at the time, had tried to make up to Jefferson for the loss of his wife. She was more mature than her years.

She knew how much letters from home meant to her father and was prompt in answering them. She knew the kind of news he wanted to hear and she sent that news. When the first blossoms appeared on the cherry trees, she wrote to tell him. When the peach trees began to leaf, she wrote him the exact day on which the buds had opened and he, amid all the strain of the growing breach with Hamilton, compared that date with the leafing of the peaches in New York gardens and found deep consolation in the reflection that though men might not know well how to run their affairs, Nature knew how to run hers.

The great mind which had addressed itself in the Declaration of Independence to asserting the rights of Man, buckled down to the task of writing a kind of Declaration of Dependence, asserting the duties of Woman in the role of wife.

"Your new condition [marriage]," he wrote to Martha, "will call for abundance of little sacrifices. But they will be greatly overpaid by the measure of affection they secure to you. The happiness of your life now depends on the continuing to please a single person. To this all other objects must be secondary, even your love for me, were it possible that could ever be an obstacle. . . . Cherish then, for me, my dear child, the affection of your husband and continue to love me as you have done, and to render my life a blessing by the prospect it may hold up to me of seeing you happy."

Martha usually found time to reply quickly to her father's letters, but Jefferson's younger daughter, Mary, who was twelve, was a poor correspondent. She hated letter writing or anything that made her sit down and concentrate in silence. She was a joyous little creature, as gay as a butterfly and possibly the only person in the whole world who could get her way with Tom Jefferson. He never pleaded with anyone half as hard as he pleaded with his little daughter and though she kept him smiling with the airs she put on, for she could act the great lady and the little girl all in the same minute, he worried about her attention to her education.

Her nickname was Polly, but at twelve she thought that rather undignified and wanted to be called by her proper name, Mary. Then having lived with her father in Paris, she decided she would prefer to be called Maria which had a certain distinction, and in her letters to her father, she always signed herself Maria Jefferson.

Tom Jefferson insisted that his young daughter should do a lot of reading and her reading should be equally balanced between books of learning and classical stories. Before leaving Monticello to take up his post of Secretary of State, he had given Polly a copy of *Don Quixote* by Cervantes—in Spanish. He also gave her a big Spanish-English dictionary and told her if she could read through the book, using the dictionary, she would soon be the master of the Spanish language.

Polly thought *Don Quixote* silly and hadn't much use for the Spanish language. But in duty to her father, she took the book and the big Spanish dictionary with her and her letters to Tom Jefferson (when she wrote them) never failed to make a mention of her struggles in translating the great classic—or the reasons why she wasn't struggling.

When he left for New York, she didn't stay at Monticello but went instead to stay with Mrs. Eppes, her aunt at their Richmond home.

In her first letter she wrote, "I have not been able to

read in Don Quixote every day, as I have been travelling ever since I saw you last, and the dictionary is too large to go in the pocket of the chariot, nor have I yet had an opportunity of continuing my music. I am now reading Robertson's 'America'." That, she knew, would please her father. At least she was reading something.

Polly wrote him one more letter in which she announced that she was now reading in *Don Quixote* every day and had also made a pudding and been given some chickens and hens. She was sorry she mentioned the pudding for it brought a letter from her father saying, "When I come to Virginia I shall insist on eating a pudding of your own making, as well as on trying other specimens of your skill. You must make the most of your time while you are with so good an aunt, who can teach you everything. We had no peas nor strawberries here 'til the 8th day of this month [June]. On the same day I heard the first whip-poor-will whistle. Swallows and martins appeared here on the 21st of April. When did they appear with you? And when had you peas, strawberries and whip-poor-wills in Virginia? Take notice hereafter whether the whip-poor-wills always come with the strawberries and peas."

When she had read this, Polly turned to her aunt. "Are you sure that Papa is Secretary of State?" she asked.

"Of course, dear," said Mrs. Eppes.

"Well, he writes as if he was Secretary of Agriculture, because all he wants to know is when we got peas and strawberries and when the whip-poor-will appeared here. I wish he'd send me some news about kings and queens and what the great ladies are wearing in New York." Polly loved kings and queens and great ladies and only ate peas when she had to, "for her health."

Polly made some inquiries from the servants and found out about the first appearance of peas and strawberries, but the birds defeated her. "As for the martins, swallows and whip-poor-wills," she wrote, "I was so taken up with my chickens that I never attended to them, and therefore cannot tell you when they came, though I was so unfortunate as to lose half of them [the chickens] for my cousin Bolling and myself have raised but thirteen between us."

Her father might have his troubles as Secretary of State, but it would be just as well if he realized that she had her troubles as a chicken farmer, and with the little chickens dying there wasn't time for listening for bird calls around the garden. And how was he able to listen for bird calls and deal with all those foreign governments as well? She loved him deeply but he was a great puzzle to her.

At the dinner table she listened to the conversation between her aunt and uncle and the guests about the revolution in France and whether the king was likely to be replaced and what attitude her father would take in such an event. There was talk of his differences, amounting to a quarrel, with a Mr. Hamilton, and Polly wondered what kind of a monster this Mr. Hamilton was who could quarrel with her father.

That spring in New York, the spring of 1790, was a bitter season of blustering winds and gales. When the winter snows had melted and turned the unpaved streets of the city into mud, the winds came and dried the mud to dust, which whipped around the narrow streets blinding and choking people.

"The gales of spring," Jefferson was told by those who had lived their lives in New York. "We can reckon on that Jersey wind from January through the end of March." They spoke about the "Jersey wind" as if the whole reason for the existence of New Jersey was to generate a wind to fling into New York, and that point of view among native New Yorkers has scarcely altered to this day. Later, discussing the affairs of that first session of the Congress with Madison, the latter picked on the phrase.

"Perhaps all we have endured here in our differences with Mr. Hamilton are but the gales of spring," Madison said. "The gales of the springtime of our republic which will be replaced by a full summer of liberty."

"I hope so, sir," said Jefferson, "but I have known spring gales to stunt summer growth and ruin autumn's harvest."

Congress adjourned in September, 1790 and Jefferson was at leave to visit Monticello. He first made a journey to Rhode Island, accompanied by President Washington. It was an inspection trip of a part of the country with which neither was familiar, but Jefferson kept his ears open and found that the agricultural part of the country had no love of monarchy or of Hamilton. Many of the small farmers had sold their script received for war service at a great discount to speculators who were now being paid in full by the government. They looked on Jefferson as the man who had tried to stand up for them and among the country folk he found himself very popular.

After the little excursion to Rhode Island with the President, Jefferson and Madison set out from New York to Virginia and stopped for a further visit with Washington at Mount Vernon. By common consent there was no talk of politics, but only of crops and livestock and the wholesome business of farming.

While he had been abroad as ambassador to France, Jefferson had sent Washington numerous packets of seeds and seedling trees for his estate at Mount Vernon. He was anxious to see how they had fared. Some were thriving, but the lucerne grass seed had not taken well at Mount Vernon. The soil was too acid for it. So the two talked soil improvement and crop rotation, which was being used with great success in England, and forgot for a while finance and political systems.

Both loved farming. Both loved their homes. Both were serving their country against their private desires, for as much as Jefferson longed to be at Monticello, Washington longed to spend the rest of his life at Mount Vernon. This was a bond which they shared and in which Hamilton had no part. He was a man of the city, a man of business and commerce with no country estate and no interest in or knowledge of farming.

Indeed, in a deep sense, Hamilton was a man from nowhere, from no place of any great worth and from no home of any happiness. His acres were the undeveloped finances of the United States and these he determined to farm as industriously as Washington and Jefferson farmed the soil of Virginia which had nourished them and their forebears for generations.

☆ 5 ☆

Thomas Jefferson remained at Monticello with his family for scarcely four weeks and then had to return on November 8, 1790 to his post as Secretary of State. He made Polly bake him a pudding which he found good and was delighted to discover that Martha, who but a year before had been a girl in a convent, was now an accomplished housewife. She looked after the running of the big household quietly and efficiently and was patient with her father who, while he liked to set a good table, could not stand waste or extravagance.

He liked to raise everything he could for his table, regretted that tea could not be grown on the slopes of the nearby mountains and had to be bought, but had a lake well stocked with fish and had long ago planted grape vines in the hope of producing his own wines. The grapes proved suitable for dessert but gave an ignoble wine which Jefferson's palate could not tolerate.

He was still sure that America could produce wines

comparable to those of France, and he had plans for starting a nail factory, nails being scarce and expensive, but these were not very far advanced. Also he was excited about a machine invented by a man called Eli Whitney for getting the seed out of cotton.

It was called a cotton gin and the design for it had been submitted to Jefferson, who besides being Secretary of State, had been put in charge of the Patent Office by Congress. He had issued a patent with delight and wrote an encouraging letter to Whitney, mentioning that he raised a little cotton himself and the whole nation should benefit from his machine.

While he was at Monticello on his brief holiday which would not last even until Christmas, he looked over some earthenware pots in which he had planted some rice seed. The seed had been gathered in the East Indies by Lieutenant William Bligh of the British Royal Navy and Jefferson had managed to get hold of a little of it. Not many years later, Lieutenant Bligh would be gathering breadfruit in Tahiti to become the victim of one of the world's most famous mutinies.

Congress began its session in the winter of 1790 in Philadelphia, the members of both the House and the Senate, having had enough of New York where prices were high, accommodation hard to come by, and the weather uncomfortable.

One of the first matters the members had to consider was some measure for raising money with which to pay off the state war debts which the nation had now taken over. Hamilton had had no vacation but had been working away on an excise bill which would provide the revenue needed. This bill would levy a tax on luxuries, specifically on whiskey. Hamilton anticipated some resistance but then there would be resistance no matter what was taxed.

Jefferson could take no interest in this matter for he had supported Hamilton's plan for taking over the state war debts and certainly money had to be raised for payment. But he knew more of the country people and particularly those of the west and south than Hamilton did, and he knew that Hamilton could hardly have picked anything more likely to make him unpopular than a tax on whiskey.

Whiskey, Jefferson knew, might be a luxury in New York or in New England where people could get French wine or rum made from West Indian molasses for their entertainment. But the pioneers of western Pennsylvania and the farmers of the Carolinas and Georgia had no ready source of wine or rum and made their own whiskey. So Hamilton's tax fell directly on the southern farmer and the western pioneer. His proposal passed the Congress over the growls of representatives from Pennsylvania and the South. Excise men were appointed to collect the tax and the mountaineers of Western Pennsylvania and Virginia looked to the priming of their muskets.

With that tax was born the feud between mountain people and revenuers that has existed to this day. Hamilton perhaps did not know, being essentially a man of the city, that whiskey distilling was a small family business which produced very little profit. His tax fell in exactly the wrong place for his own popularity. Western Americans set up secret stills in the mountain regions and whiskey became known by the then secret name of "mountain dew."

Jefferson had now known Alexander Hamilton at first hand for less than a year. He had cooperated with him on the matter of the war debts, but with the passing of the weeks and months he had grown more and more suspicious of Hamilton's aims. As Jefferson saw it, Hamilton was turning the Congress into a kind of businessman's benevolent organization. A great portion of the Congress was benefiting financially from the very measures that were passed.

Some, who a few months before, had scarcely been able to afford lodgings were ordering carriages. Others were investing in business and, it seemed to Jefferson, using their prestige as members of the Congress to get good sites and good terms for their businesses. Chambers of Commerce were being formed, all of them supporting the policies of Hamilton, and New England businessmen seemed in a fair way to be running the country that was still ninety percent agricultural.

Jefferson was not the only man who was troubled about Hamilton's influence on the Congress. Senator Maclay of Georgia snorted that the whole Congress was run by the Treasury and there was nothing he could do about it. And James Madison, who had at one time been as friendly with Hamilton as he was with Jefferson, began to avoid and oppose the brilliant Secretary of the Treasury.

Then Hamilton introduced into the Congress a bill which brought the breach between himself and Thomas Jefferson into the open. He proposed in this bill the establishment of a Bank of the United States. In essence the bank, on the authority of the government, would issue paper money which would be good for the value printed on it. Shares in the bank would be sold to subscribers at so much a share and the money thus raised would provide the financing of the bank. Those who bought the shares would of course reap the profits from the bank. In effect then the bank would be a privately owned national bank—a contradiction of terms that had Jefferson fuming.

Jefferson hated paper money. He had seen millions of dollars worth of it issued by the states during the Revolutionary War and none of it redeemable at the end of the war. He saw in Hamilton's bank a plan to put the control of the whole of the nation's finances in the hands of a powerful combination of merchants, manufacturers, and businessmen.

He opposed the bank through Madison in the Congress and personally in meetings of the Cabinet. And now he no longer spoke in quiet polite terms while facing Hamilton across the Cabinet table. He said plainly that the whole measure was unconstitutional, that if it were allowed it would ruin the nation and destroy the very fabric of the Constitution.

"Congress," he told the President, "had not the power to incorporate such a bank. The powers of the Congress are enumerated in the Constitution and all powers not so enumerated are reserved to the states or to the people. Take one step beyond the boundaries specifically drawn around the powers of Congress and you will open to the Congress a boundless field of power to which no limit may be drawn."

Washington listened deep in thought, for on the matter of the Constitution and its interpretation there was no greater authority in the land than Thomas Jefferson. Perhaps nobody else was as deeply read as he in those philosophies which relate to men and their government. Jefferson's learning in this area went back to the laws of the Anglo-Saxons, and he had even studied the archaic language of the Saxons to read and ponder their ancient institutions.

Hamilton realized that he was up against a constitutional issue. There was no constitutional question involved in the Assumption Act nor the Excise Act. But here was his great plan on which, as he saw it, the commercial wealth of the nation depended, blocked by the Constitution—or rather Jefferson's interpretation of the Constitution.

"I disagree with the Secretary of State," he said. "The Constitution plainly says that the Congress is empowered to lay taxes for the purpose of providing for the general welfare and also to make all laws necessary and proper for carrying into execution its own enumerated powers. In short, Congress is empowered to make what laws it thinks will contribute to the general welfare, and the Bank Bill will certainly qualify under that definition."

"Not so," cried Jefferson. "The powers of Congress are not so broad. They are spelled out and limited. That was purposely done. The Congress cannot make any law it pleases and bless that law by saying it is for the general welfare. Given such powers as that, the Congress could pass a law depriving four-fifths of the nation of the power to vote and say that this was done for the general welfare for four-fifths of the nation was not to be trusted! The Congress may not do anything they please to provide for the general welfare. They can only lay taxes for that purpose. The plan for a national bank does not contemplate a tax and therefore the Congress cannot constitutionally sanction such a plan."

"Will you agree, sir," asked Hamilton, "that it is in the general welfare to establish such a bank?"

"I will not, sir," said Jefferson. "Banks we must have. But they should be organized by private parties or by the state legislatures. The power to organize a bank belongs to the States and to the people. It does not belong to the Federal Government which, if your plan were passed, would make the national government an obliging junior partner in a firm of ambitious financiers."

Washington did not know on which side justice lay. He asked both Hamilton and Jefferson to submit written opinions on the legality of a nationally chartered bank. Jefferson, calling Madison to his aid, for Madison was in effect the designer of the Constitution, submitted his report enlarging the arguments he had advanced personally to Washington.

Hamilton, as hard a worker as Jefferson, submitted his report arguing for a "loose" rather than a "tight" interpretation of the powers of the Congress. In financial matters, the President tended to side with Hamilton who was as brilliant in matters of commerce and finance as Jefferson was in matters of law and government. The cabinet was split down the middle on a Constitutional issue and it was a split over which there could be no compromise.

When both reports were in, Washington studied them carefully for several days. Hamilton's bill had passed the Congress, where Madison had led the attack on it, and now lay before him for signature.

Washington consulted with Madison and asked him also for a report on the legality of the bill. But in the end he decided that Hamilton was right and signed the measure.

"We shall have," said Jefferson when he heard the news, "another South Sea Bubble.* Fortunes will now be made in paper money in the buying and selling of stock—bank stock and business stock—without one penny's worth of real gain to the nation. Gambling will replace industry as a means of acquiring wealth. Stock jobbers have taken over the nation's affairs and the only cure lies in changing the representation in Congress to give a greater say to farmers and country people."

When Jefferson analyzed the vote on the bill in the Congress, he found that though the southern representatives had voted against it, the northern representatives had voted for it and their vote had carried the bill. Here again was the dangerous division, the South versus the North. The southern planters had little use for banks. But northern businessmen needed them. The South was agricultural, the North becoming industrialized and looking to industry for its greatest increase of wealth. He feared this difference of activity and interests; feared that it might one day rend the nation apart. But there was little he could do to close the growing breach.

Jefferson's fears of a tremendous financial collapse from speculation in bank and business shares were not

* Popular name in England for the disastrous speculation in the South Sea Company which, in 1720, collapsed, causing banks to fail and ruining thousands.

immediately realized. Instead, the country entered on an enormous wave of prosperity. Many new industries were opened up. Many new houses and public buildings erected. Farmers found a ready market at a good price for their crops and the merchant marine was prospering, even though British markets were closed and French markets, due to the revolution in France, uncertain. Enterprising New England ship-owners were opening a prosperous trade with China, exchanging furs and ginseng root for silks, cloth called Nankeen cloth (because it came principally from Nanking) and earthenware.

The country was busy supplying its own wants in housing, in food and in clothing. And the people were prepared to accept the paper money issued by the Bank of the United States in payment for their goods. They felt that with the country behind the bank, the currency, even if it was only paper with a value printed on its face, was sound. They were not afraid to accept it and Hamilton was right. He had supplied the nation with a currency in which people had confidence and so the nation flourished.

But the gambling in stocks which Jefferson had feared was also under way and gathering speed. The original twenty thousand shares of bank stock were increased to twenty-four thousand and were bought up as soon as available. They were then resold at a higher price and sold again at a higher price still. And what happened with the bank stocks happened also with business stocks where the business was known to have obtained a loan from the bank. These stocks were bought quickly, their values soared, they were sold and bought again so that, as Jefferson had foreseen, fortunes were being made in the buying and selling of paper without the actual wealth of the nation being increased by as much as a cent.

How were these shares bought and sold? They were bought in the first instance with the actual cash of the nation, so that capital flowed into the northern states to buy bank and business shares, leaving the outlying parts of the country utterly short of coin. And as capital migrated to New York and Philadelphia in this flurry of speculation, land values there rose while they fell in the other states.

It was not long before many businessmen found it more profitable to buy and sell stocks and shares than to conduct their own businesses. Money that should have gone into outfitting ships and equipping factories and buying raw materials went instead into buying bank paper. Stocks were also bought with the limited paper currency the bank was authorized to issue —diverting this money to speculation when it was issued for the purposes of commerce.

Jefferson warned Washington of what was happening. "Ships are lying idle at their wharves," he said. "Buildings are left unfinished so that the funds for finishing them can be used for buying stocks. Capital is taken away from agriculture and commerce to be used in stock jobbery. There is a rage about among the people to get rich in a day. Why should a tailor work away with his needle when he can win thousands in one day by buying stock? Even if he loses it on the morrow, he will be tempted to try again."

Hamilton of course knew of this effect, but he was

sure that it would pass and he did his best to curtail it. He had not made a dollar himself in the kind of speculation of which Jefferson complained.

The palace of paper which many had built for themselves in speculation did finally come tumbling down. Colonel William Duer, Assistant Secretary of the Treasury, had invested so heavily in paper stocks of all kinds that his company could not meet its obligations. He attempted to sell some of his holdings, but in 1792 a kind of panic spread among the people when they heard that Duer was selling out.

The market was flooded with stocks and their values tumbled so that thousands were ruined overnight. There were fistfights in the streets of New York and challenges to duels and many people, wealthy citizens one day, were fugitives from their creditors the next. The collapse was big but it was neither national nor catastrophic.

Despite Jefferson's fears, the country was producing enough real wealth in the form of goods to weather the storm. The bank remained firm, the national currency paper, through it all, remained acceptable. Economically the nation was stronger than Jefferson had believed. He had lost the first round with Hamilton whose national bank, by providing a sound supply of currency, brought needed prosperity to the new nation.

Hamilton's popularity soared in the northern and eastern states. In the western and southern states, which had little industry or shipping, he was distrusted and Jefferson was the hero of the small farmer who made up the bulk of the population.

☆ 6 ☆

When he arrived in Philadelphia, Thomas Jefferson had found a pleasant house on the banks of the Schuylkill River, with a good garden around it, which he had rented for the duration of his stay in the city. There was over an acre of ground surrounding the house at his disposal and a number of lovely plane trees to shade the lawns of the garden. With the coming of spring and warm weather, he started to move the contents of his study into the garden—his writing desk, his chair, some books stacked around on tables. And in this open-air office he did much of his work and was much happier than at the official home of his department in the city.

He couldn't help improving the grounds—straightening a path here, putting a curve of hedge at another place, begging a few rose cuttings from neighbors and exchanging seeds with them. If they hadn't known he was Secretary of State, they might have mistaken him for a gentleman of leisure, intensely interested in books and horticulture.

Even weeds interested him. People often saw him going through the knee-deep spring grass, picking butterweed or other wild plants which he took back to the table under the plane trees, examined, and made pressings of in a book kept specifically for that purpose.

There was a lot of traffic up and down the Schuylkill River, which was a lovely stream in those days. The river was fished for shad and trout and bream, and waterboatmen took parties up and down the stream on outings. Travelling thus, people often saw the tall, red-haired Secretary of State, his stockings and knee breeches dusted with the pollen of marsh marigolds which flourished on the banks, picking the wild flowers of the meadow. They didn't think him eccentric or mad. They respected him far too much for that, for this was the man who had written the Declaration of Independence.

"What isn't he interested in?" they asked each other, and the boatmen would shake their heads and recount how Mr. Jefferson often hailed them to question them about the river and the life in it.

"Wants to know when we took the first shad and what was the biggest ever caught and what date it was caught on," they said. "And when we first see mayfly on the water and whether we catch as many fish now as our fathers caught. Why, there isn't a thing in the world that Mr. Jefferson hasn't got some interest in."

That was certainly the truth. Harassed as he was, and full of foreboding over Hamilton's bank and the speculation in paper, Jefferson still had time to make notes of the migrations of birds and the hatching times of insects and the mid-day temperatures of Philadelphia.

His daughters were still poor correspondents by his standards and he berated them for not writing to him. He was particularly upset about his eldest daughter, Martha, or Patsy as she was called. When he left Monticello in the previous November, she had told him she was expecting a baby. And for weeks she didn't write him a word on the subject. He became anxious but his anxieties were put at rest early in February when Patsy wrote him that her baby was a girl and she and the baby were well.

He was immediately full of advice on the subject of motherhood, telling her to take the greatest care not to expose herself and catch a cold. On the other hand it would be well to get out into the fresh air; if she started a garden that would be the best way of achieving this.

Polly, though she loved her father deeply, still hated writing letters and was still struggling to get through *Don Quixote*—in Spanish. But she did write to say the baby was very pretty and had deep blue eyes. By return mail Jefferson wrote her, forgiving her for her lack of letters and telling her that he saw blackbirds on the 27th of February and robin red-breasts on the 7th of March and also heard frogs for the first time that year.

"Oh dear," said Polly when she got this letter. "Spring again. And now its frogs." But Jefferson was relentless. He loved nature so much himself that he assumed that everybody else shared this interest. And because he lived this full life shared with all the living things of the earth, it was important to him to know whether the frogs of Virginia sang their spring song before the frogs of Pennsylvania. He was soon writing Polly again the whole details of the pageant of the coming of spring.

Bluebirds had followed the frogs, appearing in the woodlands around on March 17th. The very next day the weeping willow before his house had put out its first leaflets. The lilac and gooseberry had started to leaf on the 25th of March and the golden willow on the 26th.

It was all so exciting to him, filling him with happiness and strength, for there was a continuum here that swallowed up all the petty quarrels of men. Bluebirds and blackbirds and lilacs and golden willow; the grass coming on well and shad in the river and a new kind of flowering bean which produced a beautiful blossom. These were the riches of the world, given in abundance every year and the only riches he cared for. He sent some of the beans to Martha to encourage her to start her garden so she could recover quickly from child bearing. He begged her to take good care of them, to nourish them with her own hand, so that there would be plenty of seed from them in the late summer.

He lived alone, except for his servants, in the house by the Schuylkill River, with the lilacs and the golden willow and the gooseberry patch and he needed someone to share these things with him. So he thought of James Madison and invited him to come and board with him.

Madison had his kind of mind and was interested in everything, and Jefferson held out a further bait.

Cases of books had arrived from France and he was setting up a library in the house where Madison could have free run of all the books.

Thomas Jefferson had no sons and Madison had become like a son to him. Madison, as a boy, had been so sickly that the doctors had been quite sure he would never survive to manhood and he had often heard them express this opinion to his parents.

Being sure then that he would not be long in the world, and that the first serious illness would carry him off, he had decided to make the very best use of the few years that lay ahead of him. He had therefore plunged himself into learning; he couldn't play games or go on fishing or hunting expeditions because of the delicacy of his health.

He got his adventures out of reading, and by the time he was in his teens his learning on almost any subject rivalled that of a professor. He had gone to the College of New Jersey (now Princeton) and studied law and theology. He was a master of Greek, Latin and Hebrew and believed, like Jefferson, that men by birth possessed certain rights such as freedom of conscience, and freedom of speech, which no government should ever take from them.

But he was not greatly interested in botany. At least he was not interested in botany as botany. But botany as politics had a certain appeal to James Madison. And so, one day, he called on Jefferson at the house by the river and exulted over the coming of spring and smiled as Jefferson assured him that the gelder-rose and dogwood and redbud and azaleas were sure to blossom in the first week in May.

"I find," said Jefferson, "though Polly is not the best correspondent on the subject, that spring is two weeks earlier in Virginia than in Pennsylvania."

"I wonder how New York compares," said Madison.

"New York?" echoed Jefferson.

"Yes. New York. It would be interesting to know whether the redbud blossomed in the first week in May in New York and whether the lilac was in bloom by the last of April. Why not a trip together into the New York countryside to see how spring is coming there?"

"With all my heart," said Jefferson, "I would like nothing better. We could go up to Albany and then to Lake George. I have never seen it and am told it is one of the most beautiful of our lakes."

"And then we could go on to Bennington and so through Vermont to the Connecticut River, and down the river to Hartford and then back to New York and so return to Philadelphia," said Madison. "There is not much sense in setting our foot upon the road and not travelling the fullest possible distance."

"Come," said Jefferson. "I have a map. We will trace the whole route. We shall have good horses and fine summer roads, and take a meal in the grass by the roadside and forget about politics."

"Right," said Madison. "But of course courtesy will demand that we call on Governor George Clinton of New York. And we would be wanting in breeding if we did not call upon the governors of Massachusetts and Vermont as well."

"Mr. Madison," said Jefferson, a suspicion beginning to form in his mind, "are you sure that we are undertaking this trip in the interests of botany?"

"Mr. Jefferson," replied Madison with a slight

smile, "you have your botany and I have mine. I would remind you that next year there is an election, and votes like flowers require cultivation. We must, sir, bring something of the countryside into the Congress."

Jefferson looked searchingly into his friend's face. "Tell me," he said, "is your mind never without a political plan?"

"Sir," said Madison, "politics is a science as stimulating as horticulture. America is a garden. Let us look to its cultivation and sow a few seeds of a republican kind. I can attend to that while you classify the wild flowers and make notes of the time of their first appearance."

And so the two of them—tall Thomas Jefferson and wizened little James Madison—planned a most peculiar botany trip which would take them into the northern states where Jefferson lacked information on the flora and fauna. And Madison lacked congressional votes for Jefferson's programs.

☆ 7 ☆

Thomas Jefferson left Philadelphia on May 16, 1791 for his botanizing tour through the New England states. He met James Madison in New York and they set off together up the Hudson River to Albany and then Lake George which Jefferson thought the most beautiful body of water he had ever seen.

The lake was crystal clear and the steep banks rich with groves of white pine, silver fir, aspen and paper birch. The paper birch fascinated Jefferson and he had soon acquired a book with leaves made of the bark of the tree and it was on this that he wrote his letters to his daughters. He fished in the lake with Madison, catching speckled trout, salmon, trout and bass. He weighed them all and made notes of the weights and sailed on the lake in a passenger sloop which then went on to Lake Champlain.

But Lake Champlain was a disappointment. The water was turbulent and muddy, the surface of the lake windswept and the fishing very poor. Jefferson and Madison sailed on Lake Champlain for a day and u lull, but head winds prevented the vessel getting to the north end of the lake, so they put about and came back down the river to pleasant Lake George again.

The weather was monstrously hot. "As sultry and hot as could be found in Carolina or Georgia," Jefferson said in a letter to Patsy. And he was not above praising the weather of his native Virginia as compared to that of New York where he said there was six months of winter and then a sudden tropical summer. "Spring and autumn, which make a paradise of our country, are rigorous winter with them," he told Maria and added a little smugly that strawberries were only just in blossom, whereas in Virginia the strawberry season was already over.

He had been suffering from severe headaches before he started the trip, headaches which lasted without relief for several days and nights. But once he was on the road with Madison they vanished so he knew that they came from overwork and over-worry and he was happy to make that discovery. But he kept up the habit of bathing his feet in a basin of cold water every morning and found the dawn water of Lake George delicious for this purpose.

Meanwhile, of course, there were the necessary courtesy calls to be made on men of local eminence. There was a talk with Governor George Clinton of New York and also with the Revolutionary War hero, Aaron Burr, who was becoming influential in an organization called the Sons of St. Tammany. This was a social group, not yet a political society, which advocated republican as opposed to aristocratic principles. Tammany, then, supported Jefferson's views as distinct from those of Hamilton, for Hamilton was related by marriage to the powerful Schuyler family which dominated New York politics. Jefferson found Burr ambitious, thrusting and rash, and did not quite trust him though he was too polite to show any dislike.

"Mr. Burr," he said to Madison, "seems on the democratic side to be what Mr. Hamilton is on the monarchist or federal side. In short I am not certain whether he is a republican by persuasion or a republican by ambition."

"For the time being, sir," said Madison, "it is surely sufficient that he is republican in a state where republicans are sorely needed. He has, as you know, a magnificent war record."

"I don't doubt his patriotism for a moment," said Jefferson, "but ambitious men often persuade themselves that what will advance their careers will also advance their country's cause. I do not find it in my heart to completely trust him."

With Governor Clinton, Jefferson was open in his distrust of what he called the monarchical tendency of Hamilton and those who supported him. The Vice President, John Adams, he said, seemed to have been dazzled by the glories of the English court when he had been in London and believed that, cleaned of its corruption, the British Constitution with a sovereign at the head of the government was the best that could be devised. Washington, of course, was solidly republican, but he wasn't aware of the effect on others of the court atmosphere that surrounded him.

"And would you favor the re-election of Mr. Adams as Vice President?" asked Governor Clinton. "We know that you are attached to him. Your career and his have gone forward side by side since the day you met at the second Continental Congress. You were in Paris together, you were in England together [though only for a while], and now you are in the administration together. Come, sir, be open with us. Do you feel personally indebted to Mr. Adams in the matter of his re-election to the Vice Presidency?"

"You misread my nature if you think that personal feelings would affect me in matters of national interest," said Jefferson. "I believe the country to be at a time of crisis. I believe that the future of the republic may well hinge on the result of the election next year. I believe that for Vice President we must have a man about whose devotion to the republican form of government there is no shadow of doubt."

That was all that was said. But out of the meeting came a tacit agreement that Clinton would oppose Adams for the Vice Presidency the following year with at least the silent approval of Thomas Jefferson.

Madison and Jefferson then returned to Philadelphia, Jefferson with several valises of plant specimens and Madison with his valises figuratively stuffed with New York votes.

When they got back to Pennsylvania, Madison had another proposal for Jefferson. There was only one big political newspaper published at the time, *The Gazette of the United States,* with a circulation of fourteen hundred. It was Hamilton's paper in that it ardently supported every proposal of the Secretary of the Treasury who, indeed, wrote many articles for it. These articles were published under pen names.

In some of them Hamilton attacked Jefferson, even

accusing him of lack of patriotism and seeking, by opposing the Bank Bill, to wreck the credit of the nation. The editor of this newspaper was John Fenno, a man whom Hamilton had once saved from bankruptcy. He was utterly loyal to Hamilton and completely hostile to Jefferson. Fenno was also a convinced monarchist. "Take away thrones and crowns from among men and there will soon be an end of all dominion and justice," he once wrote and that summed up his creed on government.

Madison now suggested, for the first time, to Jefferson that it was time there was an opposition newspaper to give the republican point of view—Jefferson's point of view.

"There is a gentleman, Philip Morin Freneau, once a classmate of mine, an ardent republican and one who would make an excellent editor for such a paper," said Madison. "He is an accomplished linguist, a poet, and a journalist. Why not offer him a position in your department as a translating clerk? With a salary to meet his needs, he could then undertake the publishing of a newspaper which would answer Hamilton's *Gazette*."

All that Jefferson would do was write to Freneau, offering him the job as translating clerk in the State Department. "The salary indeed is very low, being but two hundred and fifty dollars a year," he wrote, "but also it gives so little to do as not to interfere with any other calling the person [who takes the post] may choose."

Freneau refused the post. He wanted something firmer, an assurance of support from the Secretary of State for the projected newspaper. And indeed, Jefferson had not even mentioned starting a newspaper. He had merely written of a low-salaried post as a translator in the State Department.

Madison consulted with Jefferson, but Jefferson was not going to use his position to start a newspaper though Hamilton was using his to support one. However he did agree to write to Madison just what kind of help he could give Freneau, if Freneau came to Philadelphia and if Freneau did decide to start a republican publication.

He would have access to all the foreign correspondence of the State Department. He would be able to see all the foreign newspapers that reached Jefferson through the mails, sent by his friends in Europe as well as by the various agents, ministers and ambassadors of the United States. And to finance the newspaper, Jefferson would give Freneau the business of publishing all proclamations and public notices that came from his department and were required by law to be published in a newspaper of general circulation. If that were put all together with his guaranteed salary, Freneau should be able to do very well.

Madison conveyed these views to his friend Freneau, who finally agreed, came to Philadelphia and, in October of 1791, began to publish the *National Gazette,* bringing an edition out twice a week.

The result was that the quarrels of the cabinet between Hamilton and Jefferson were now brought out into the open, laid before the public in the two newspapers—the *Gazette of the United States,* Hamilton's newspaper, and the *National Gazette,* Jefferson's newspaper.

There was one difference, however, between Hamilton and Jefferson in their relationship to these party newspapers. Jefferson never told Freneau what to put in his newspaper, did not see the articles before publication and never wrote a word for it. Hamilton however was a kind of editor-in-chief of Fenno's paper, writing many of the editorials himself, and writing many articles on public affairs which were printed under pen names though everybody soon knew that the author was Alexander Hamilton.

Up to this point there had been differences between the Secretary of the Treasury and the Secretary of State—differences in principle which ran all the way from the form of government to the national finance program. But now there began to appear two distinct parties in American political life—a party which supported Hamilton and became known as the Federalists, and a party which supported Jefferson and which became known as Democratic-Republicans, later called the Republicans. It was not, however, the ancestor of the Republican Party of today.

Freneau was too brilliant a man to try to refute the cleverly reasoned articles of Alexander Hamilton. He knew that the public would not follow astute reasoning closely. The way to bring Hamilton down was to ridicule him, and Freneau was a master of ridicule.

During the Revolutionary War Freneau had built a ship at his own expense, armed it, and set out to fight the British. His vessel, the *Aurora*, was sunk in an engagement and he was taken a prisoner and put on one of the horrid prison ships of the time. He wrote a sardonic verse of four lines, summarizing his views of the Hessian doctor who attended the sick of the prison ship:

"Here, uncontrolled, he exercised his trade,
And grew experienced by the deaths he made;
By frequent blows we from his cane endured,
He killed at least as many as he cured."

The name of the brutal doctor who caned sick and wounded men is lost. But the infamy of the prison ships has endured through two hundred years because of Freneau's lines.

It was this talent for satire that Freneau now turned against Hamilton who, like many men of genius, was a victim of pride. He could scarcely tolerate an argument that ran against his own reasoning for he took all things personally. Freneau, a small stooped, slight man with the spirit of a poet and the heart of a sea captain, knew this weakness and stabbed vigorously and repeatedly at Hamilton's reputation.

His attacks drove Hamilton to cold fury. For the Secretary of the Treasury to be publicly pilloried by a clerk in the State Department was more than he could stand. He was convinced that Jefferson was behind the attacks and in his anger he committed a grave error. He himself replied to Freneau's taunts, though under the nameless signature "An American."

He accused Freneau of being a henchman of Thomas Jefferson, said he was being paid with government funds, that although he was employed as a translating clerk, he was ignorant of the French language. And then Hamilton turned on Jefferson and in the same article accused him of being in effect an enemy of the government and of advocating "national disunion, national insignificance, public disorder and discredit."

Jefferson read this attack, knew—as indeed the whole of Philadelphia knew—who was the author, but disdained to reply. He didn't have to reply, for Freneau undertook that task with delight. He voluntarily appeared before the mayor of Philadelphia and took an oath asserting that Jefferson had not hired him to edit a newspaper, had nothing to do with the newspaper, never wrote a line for it nor influenced the writing of a line in it. He, Freneau, was completely "free, unfettered and uninfluenced."

The step was a bold one, for if any of the statements he made under oath could be proved untrue then, under the law of the time, Freneau was liable to heavy fine and imprisonment for false swearing. Hamilton finally had to retract his charges, for to persist in them now rendered him open to an action for libel. He found to his chagrin that he had challenged not Thomas Jefferson, a worthy opponent, but a mere translating clerk. The challenge had been public and he had been defeated.

The one man who was caught in the middle of this Cabinet fight conducted in the public press was George Washington. He was greatly disturbed to find the two senior members of his Cabinet at each other's throats in the daily press, with the public taking sides. He had hoped for unity in his Cabinet and thought Hamilton and Jefferson would become a brilliant team working together for the benefit of the country—one in the field of finance and the other in the field of foreign affairs which were daily becoming more important.

Some time earlier, Washington had confided to James Madison, who although but a member of the

Congress, was so highly thought of that he had the President's confidence, that he wanted to retire. He did not want to run for a second term and he asked Madison to consider when it would be best to make an announcement that he wouldn't be a candidate for the Presidency in the coming election.

"If I make the announcement too early, people will think I have done so in order to be coaxed into changing my mind," said Washington. "If I make it too late, it will not be fair to others who may wish to seek the office. The timing of the announcement is very important and I wish you would advise me when you think would be the best time to make it."

Madison was deeply disturbed at the prospect and said so. But Washington was firm. He started to speculate on a successor and asked Madison whether he thought Jefferson would run for the office—or if not run for it, accept it if the vote went in that direction.

"I am sure that he will not," said Madison. "He wants nothing more than to return to his home, to his philosophy and his farming. He has a deep repugnance for public life. His ambition lies in Monticello, not in Philadelphia."

"And mine lies in Mount Vernon and not here," said Washington. "I have spent more years in the public service than I can well afford. I am almost sixty, Mr. Madison, and I want to go back to my home."

When Jefferson heard that Washington was determined not to be a candidate for re-election, he pleaded with him to change his mind.

"The country is divided now worse than it has ever been," said Jefferson. "Only one man can bring unity and that man is you. All others are partisan and you must, whether you wish it or not, serve again. Under anyone else, the nation will be rent asunder."

On the point that Washington must serve a second term Hamilton agreed with Jefferson. It was the only point on which the two giants did agree, and in the interest of preventing a national split between warring parties, Washington reluctantly agreed to serve for a second term, if elected.

He had hardly made the decision, before the enmity between his two chief lieutenants broke into the public press. He was angered and felt betrayed, and he wrote a letter to Jefferson and another to Hamilton, asking them to compose their differences.

Jefferson had returned to Monticello, for the Congress had at last wound up its business and he received Washington's letter there. Washington's was a polite and restrained letter, a plea for cooperation within the government. But Jefferson was in no mood to accept the President's advice to put aside differences in the national good. He wrote a reply of some three thousand words in which he denounced Hamilton's policies and defended himself against Hamilton's attacks.

Hamilton had asserted that he was hostile to the Constitution. "False," said Jefferson. "No man approved every tittle of the Constitution. My objection . . . was that it lacked a bill of rights securing freedom of religion, freedom of the press, freedom from standing armies, trial by jury and a constant Habeas Corpus act. Colonel Hamilton's was that it did not provide for a king and a house of lords. The sense of America has approved my objection and added a Bill of Rights, not the king and lords."

He defended freedom of the press and both Fenno's and Freneau's rights to publish newspapers of opposing views. "No government ought to be without censors and where the press is free, no one ever will," he wrote.

He concluded his letter by announcing that he himself wished to retire from office. But when he retired and was again a private citizen, he would feel justified in defending himself from Hamilton's attacks.

Some of his fury against Hamilton came out as he referred to him as a man "whose history . . . is a tissue of machinations against the liberty of the country which has not only received and given him bread, but heaped its honors on his head."

It was not like Jefferson to hold a man's origins against him, but his anger against Hamilton could not be contained. It was more than anger. It was white hot indignation at the thought of an immigrant wrecking the liberties of the nation that had taken him in.

Three weeks after he sent this letter off, and with Congress about to convene again in Philadelphia, Jefferson called on Washington at Mount Vernon.

Washington pleaded with Jefferson not to insist on retiring. "I myself wished to retire, as you know," he said. "You persuaded me to be a candidate for reelection in the national interest. I agreed. I now ask you, also in the national interest, to serve again as Secretary of State. I need your views in the Cabinet as a counter check to those of Mr. Hamilton. I am not partisan. You are both needed, one to balance the other."

"I am a Republican. Mr. Hamilton favors a monarchy," said Jefferson. "I cannot work with such a man nor agree with him. There is a strong tide of monarchy and aristocracy running through the country and it is the work of Mr. Hamilton."

"Come, sir," said the President, "I think you exaggerate. I doubt that there are ten men in the country, whose opinions are worth attention, who entertain the thought of a monarchy here."

"There are more than you think," said Jefferson. "Even though the mass of the people may be soundly republican there is a big organized group who favor a monarchy, and Mr. Hamilton is one of them. There are very many men in the Congress who have benefited substantially from Hamilton's financial policies and they are therefore ready to do anything that he asks."

Washington admitted that this was the case but that such conditions could not be avoided in any government. He said the nation had benefited greatly from Hamilton's financial policies and asked Jefferson once again to consider his decision to retire.

They parted without Jefferson giving any promise on the subject.

☆ 8 ☆

President Washington had also written to Hamilton asking him to drop the press campaign against Jefferson. He wanted to know whether it was true that Hamilton himself had written some of the articles attacking Jefferson. Hamilton admitted that this was so but he could not promise not to write any more. The battle in the press had reached such a point that he could not withdraw. And so Washington was left with no peace in sight between his two ministers and not even a promise from Jefferson that he would continue to serve as Secretary of State.

It was James Madison who convinced Jefferson that he must remain in office. "You cannot retire under fire," he said. "It will not do to resign your office and then attempt to reply to Hamilton when you are a private citizen. Your retirement would merely give Hamilton the victory he seeks and your replies would be ineffective."

Washington wanted Jefferson not merely in the cabinet but also to make his peace with Hamilton. But the man who had written the Declaration of Independence, throwing off the authority of the English king, could not come to terms with one who wanted to substitute for the English King George an American King George. He withdrew his resignation but made it clear to the President that he considered it his duty to oppose Hamilton in every way.

Against this background the election campaign of 1792 was bitter. Jefferson coined the word "monocrat" for Hamilton and his followers, meaning that they sought rule through one person who would be a kind of a dictator.

Vice President John Adams made no secret of the fact that he favored the British system and coined the word "mobocracy" to describe the followers of Jefferson, meaning that these were people who favored rule by an illiterate and irresponsible mob in the name of democracy. Adams knew that Governor Clinton of New York was a candidate for the Vice Presidency with Jefferson's support. The two old friends who had stood close together in the days of the Revolution now began to drift apart from each other and would soon be enemies.

It was in this election that what became known later as a political machine first came into crude being. Hamilton's political machine consisted of the Chambers of Commerce and their influential members established throughout the eastern and northern states. All supported him. Jefferson, representing noncommercial America, had no such ready-made groups to turn to. The small farmers, the frontiersmen, the little country merchants and craftsmen were not organized into any kind of group. Jefferson knew they believed as he did. But how to unite them presented a huge problem.

Sitting under the plane trees in his garden at Philadelphia, he talked the matter over with Madison. It was Madison, with his keen political brain, who suggested the solution.

"We had a similar problem in the days before the Revolution," he said. "Then many were on our side but were not united. The solution was the Committee of Correspondence which passed out news of the struggle for freedom to leading men throughout the colonies who saw to it that this news received the widest circulation. We must do the same now."

And so Jefferson started writing letters to the principal men in the states who could be relied upon to support him. He asked them to do whatever lay in their power to influence the election to the Congress of men who supported his own views.

In Maryland he made contact with John Francis Mercer; in North Carolina, William Jones of Halifax and Nathaniel Macon. South Carolina was dominated by wealthy Charleston merchants but Jefferson found a friend in Charles Pinckney whose cousin, Thomas Pinckney, Jefferson soon appointed United States Minister to Great Britain.

He had already done what he could in New York and he had plenty of supporters in Pennsylvania and his native Virginia. This was the extent of Jefferson's electioneering.

The newspapers of the country led by those of Fenno and Freneau aired the issues of the election so that the voters could make up their own minds where they stood.

When the votes were counted Jefferson had achieved a significant victory. To be sure John Adams was re-elected Vice President but Governor Clinton had piled up an impressive number of votes for that office. Indeed Adams, a far greater figure than Clinton, counted only twenty-seven more votes than Clinton and what pleased Jefferson was that New York, previously devoted to Hamilton, had voted for Clinton as Vice President. The botanizing trip had paid off.

More important, Jefferson's supporters had won a majority of the seats in the Congress. The one-sided connection between Congress and commerce which had in Jefferson's view made Congress merely a tool of the Secretary of the Treasury had been weakened if not broken. Congress, Jefferson believed, could now start acting as an independent body.

There was one complete surprise for Jefferson in the election returns. Kentucky, a new state on the far western frontier, had cast all its votes for Jefferson as Vice President. The votes were, of course, thrown away, but they heartened Thomas Jefferson who saw the future of America not in the wealthy eastern cities of the New England states but in the western wildernesses over the mountains.

Jefferson was not long in making use of his new strength in the Congress. He wanted the Congress to shake itself free of the Treasury and Hamilton. He wanted money bills to be originated in the Congress and not in the Treasury.

The thing to do, he decided, was to have the Congress demand a statement from Hamilton of the condition of the Treasury Department. It was not long before a young Virginian, Congressman William B.

Giles, was demanding, on the floor of the House, on Jefferson's instigation, a complete statement of the affairs of the Treasury Department. Giles was supported by Madison and they presented a set of resolutions calling on the President to give a detailed report on the government's money.

There were no objections to the resolutions. They were adopted and Hamilton, who had got into the habit of telling the Congress what he wanted in the way of money bills, was now on the defensive. He now had to report to the Congress, not the Congress to him.

Hamilton turned his tremendous energy to compiling a report of the finances of the nation down to the last penny. Within twelve days he sent his first report to the House detailing in elaborate tables, the expenditures of his department.

Two days later he sent in another report. Within a week a third report was in the hands of the legislators still struggling through the tables contained in the first. Another week and his last report was in, bringing everything up to the minute. In less than a month the amazing Hamilton in four voluminous reports, had rendered a complete account to the House of every penny of the nation's money.

As soon as each of these reports came in Jefferson went over them, and Madison, too. They found no evidence of corruption but they did find that Hamilton had been somewhat high-handed in the handling of the nation's money. Money approved by the Congress for one purpose had been used by Hamilton for other purposes. He had used funds voted by the Congress to pay off interest on old loans.

An attempt to censure Hamilton was voted down

after a prolonged debate in Congress. But the nation's newspapers had fully informed the public that while Hamilton might not be corrupt he was something of an autocrat. In handling public funds he considered that he knew better than the Congress.

That was enough for Thomas Jefferson. He had made his point and made it publicly. And so the issue of the first public duel between the two men was a draw. Hamilton had tried to drive Jefferson out of the government by writing anonymous articles against him in the press. Jefferson had tried to drive Hamilton out of the government by a Congressional investigation of his department. Both men were still in the government.

Their next clash would not be on a domestic matter but on a matter of foreign policy. Figuratively the battlefield would not be Philadelphia but Paris.

☆ 9 ☆

The first two years of Thomas Jefferson's term as Secretary of State were taken up more with domestic than foreign affairs. He saw liberty threatened more at home than abroad and so concentrated his energies on the home front. But his office was that of the nation's foreign minister and so he kept closely in touch with events in Britain and in France—and with what was happening on America's western frontier along the Ohio River and the Mississippi where Britain, France and Spain were powers to be reckoned with.

In warm weather he worked under the plane trees by his house. He had his breakfast there, his lunch there and his dinner there and only returned indoors for the night.

"I never before knew the full value of trees," he wrote to Martha. "What would I not give that the trees planted nearest the house at Monticello were full grown."

Under the trees he received visitors—politicians, inventors, planters, merchants and even Indians. He had always admired the Indians. He had studied their languages. He treated them not as savages but as his equal, and when one Indian chief, Otchakitz, who had been a friend of Lafayette's during the Revolutionary war years, died in Philadelphia, Thomas Jefferson, American Secretary of State, attended the simple funeral, standing head bowed among the Indians, while the chief was buried upright as was the custom of the tribe.

The Indians respected him so much that one, a member of the Piora tribe, now extinct, named his son Jefferson. And this warrior, coming to Philadelphia with a delegation of his people, called on Jefferson under the plane trees, smoked a solemn pipe of tobacco and reported that his son was now a fine boy.

Jefferson could carry on a conversation of sorts in several Indian tongues. He compiled a dictionary of Indian words, was impressed by the fact that the Delaware word for rain *suuhlan* was close to the Monsi word *su-he-laan* and speculated that the two nations were once one. He regarded the Indian tribes as nations with whom it was his duty to deal as Secretary of State.

Visiting chieftains left him with gifts of packets of seed and instructions for planting, and from his Indian visitors he got information about the western lands beyond the Ohio to which his mind turned constantly. He believed that America must enlarge its frontiers westward, and though he mentioned this to nobody, was forming the view that the proper western limit of the United States of America was the Pacific Ocean.

But as Thomas Jefferson entered his third year as Secretary of State, it was not the western but the eastern frontier that provided the prime problem in foreign affairs. Europe loomed far larger than the Mississippi and the vast lands beyond it. And in Europe the affairs of France loomed the largest. All America was watching France where a revolution had broken out which it was hoped would establish in France the kind of freedom that was enjoyed in America.

Prominent in the French Revolution was the great friend of America, and the particularly close friend of Thomas Jefferson and George Washington—the Marquis de Lafayette. He had fought in the Continental Army, helped to wrest freedom from Britain for the United States, and had returned to his own country to establish the same measure of freedom there. Washington and Jefferson wished him well, and Jefferson, who had until recently been the United States Minister to France, was quite sure that the revolution in that country would soon be crowned with victory.

"Within a year," he had told old Benjamin Franklin on his return from Paris, "France will be as free as we are. To be sure, they will retain their monarchy. But the king's powers will be so reduced that he will be but a figure to unite the loyalty of the country."

In this prophecy, Jefferson was quite wrong. It was a prophecy perfectly in tune with his nature, but he made a great error in judging the French situation. His error lay in part in thinking that all men were as reasonable as he himself. He knew that there were differences between the leaders of the French Revolution, but he was convinced that reasonable men would iron out their differences with quiet minds in mutual trust. There were few quiet minds and little trust in France at the time.

Another mistake he made was to assume that the mass of the French people—the peasants and the sans-culottes (meaning literally, those without breeches, who could not afford such an article and wore knee-length smocks) would be content with a gradual relaxation of the terrible restrictions on their liberty.

If their taxes were lightened, if they were able to keep more of their own harvests, if they were given a measure of say in their government, they would accept these things and try, through their representatives, to gain further liberties. But the French peasants and in particular the wretched mobs of Paris, unlike the small farmers of America in pre-Revolutionary days, were illiterate. They were utterly ignorant of the whole process of government, except that they were serfs of their lord and must do whatever their lord demanded of them. The only freedom lay in getting rid of their aristocratic masters. That was all they could understand on the subject of government. Any other measure was not to be trusted.

Initially, while Jefferson was still in Paris, it had looked as though the French Revolution would be achieved with comparatively little bloodshed. To be sure, the Bastille had been stormed by the people of Paris and the heads of a few aristocrats had been paraded through the streets on pikes, but Lafayette had been put in charge of the National Guard, which meant that he was in charge of the armed forces of the revolution. Such a man would not allow widespread slaughter. Indeed, Lafayette welcomed the storming of the Bastille and sent the key of that terrible prison to his friend, George Washington, who kept it in his home at Mount Vernon.

Lafayette was loyal to his king, never for a moment visualized France without a king, and believed only that the king's power and those of the nobles should be reduced and the powers of the people increased. That done, France would be free and prosper.

But the king, Louis XVI, grew to dislike Lafayette and would not trust him. Whatever advice the young Marquis gave to his monarch, the king discounted. Indeed, the king listened only to his willful and pretty wife, Marie Antoinette, daughter of the Emperor of Austria. And she was unprepared to relinquish a particle of the royal powers. The king was forced to grant increased and more powerful representation to the mass of Frenchmen, but contrived to undo this work behind the scenes.

He was a young king and a foolish one. His hobbies were hunting, drinking and making locks and Jefferson thought him a worthless individual and the queen no better. But Jefferson believed that Lafayette and the Viscount de Noailles and other liberal French aristocrats would, through reforms of the law, achieve an almost bloodless revolution.

He had his own minister in Paris—Gouverneur Morris and of course received reports from him of affairs in France. But Morris was at heart a monarchist and therefore more aligned with Hamilton and the Federalists than with Jefferson's Democratic-Republicans. The view he took of the progress of the French Revolution often conflicted with the view the Marquis of Lafayette gave in his many letters to Jefferson. Jefferson tended to believe Lafayette and discount the views of his own minister. For a while the facts supported Jefferson.

The French Constitution was revised to give more power to the mass of the people. The king approved the new Constitution. He became a constitutional rather than a despotic monarch and was for a while enormously popular. He had been taken by the people of Paris, in a mob, from Versailles and lodged in the Tuilleries inside the city. He regarded himself secretly, however, as a prisoner, signing things under duress and planned to escape. He was recaptured and brought back to Paris.

In the meantime the direction of the revolution was slipping out of the hands of Lafayette and his friends. Various groups began to be organized who represented the mass of the French working men and peasants. They called themselves Jacobins, because their Paris headquarters were in a monastery formerly occupied by monks of that name. These Jacobin clubs wanted to sweep aside not only the king but the aristocracy as well. Aristocrats were arrested and imprisoned on a charge of "conspiring to betray the revolution." Some were undoubtedly guilty but many were innocent.

Then war broke out between France and Austria, and Austrian troops invaded French territory. The Jacobins saw in this a plot by the king and the nobles to bring in a foreign army to crush the French Revolution. The long pent-up anger of the French peasants then erupted terribly.

The Swiss Guards, a regiment of professional soldiers

whose duty it was to protect the king's person, were hacked to pieces. Semi-official courts were established on the authority of the mob to try the aristocrats who were now overflowing the prisons of Paris. For three days and nights a horrible butchery took place in Paris. The courts met in the prison grounds. Aristocrats were dragged from their cells, accused, condemned and ordered transferred to the prison of La Force for execution. They never got there.

As they left the prison gates they had to run a gauntlet of a mob armed with axes, pitchforks, and scythes—the terrible weapons of the farm. They were cut down and hacked to pieces. The gutters around these prisons ran with blood and wine, for the mob refreshed itself for its butchery work from casks of wine. Over a thousand occupants of one prison were killed in this manner before the butchery stopped. It stopped because there were no more people left to butcher. The next several days were spent in burying the bodies in graves filled with quicklime.

When news of this atrocity reached the United States, the Federalists turned on Jefferson. What had he to say now about mobocracy? Wasn't what had happened in Paris proof that people were unfit to govern themselves; that if the mass of people were given power or seized power they would destroy all who had at one time exercised any authority over them? The mob was not to be trusted and the best form of government was an enlightened monarchy supported by nobles but with representation for the lower classes—provided they were people of property. People with no property, like the French sansculottes, were not to be trusted.

Jefferson hated bloodshed. He was a man of peace and of reason. But if it were necessary to shed blood for freedom to be achieved, then he agreed with bloodshed. No price was too great to pay for liberty. The blood that had been shed in Paris in the interests of liberty was a very small drop compared with the ocean of blood that had been shed through the centuries for the support of tyrants. That was his view and he did not attempt to hide it.

There was worse to come. The Jacobins were now in power in France. All aristocrats were suspect. Even so proven a friend of freedom as Lafayette was suspect since he was an aristocrat. The young Marquis was denounced by the National Assembly and fled to Holland, horrified by the forces that had been loosed in France, but he was captured by the Austrians at Rochefort and imprisoned at Olinutz.

Uncertainty about the fate of Lafayette, whom he loved as a son, drove Washington to distraction. He wrote to Lafayette's wife, the Marchioness de Lafayette, "If I had words that could convey to you an adequate idea of my feelings on the present situation of the Marquis de Lafayette, this letter would appear to you in a different garb. The sole object in writing to you now is to inform you that I have deposited in the hands of Mr. Nicholas Van Staphurst of Amsterdam two thousand three hundred and ten guilders, Holland currency, equal to two hundred guineas, subject to your orders.

"This sum is, I am certain, the least I am indebted for services rendered me by the Marquis de Lafayette, of which I never yet have received the account."

The Jacobins were now all powerful. They announced that the king was to be tried for treason, for conspiring with foreign powers to invade France and put him back on his throne.

He was tried, found guilty and on January 24, 1793, beheaded. The news of the beheading of the French king was a long time in getting to the United States. The winter gales were so fierce that for months scarcely a ship arrived from Europe in any port of the United States. When the weather moderated and ships began to arrive, they brought terrible news. Not only had Louis XVI been beheaded, but France was at war with Britain and Spain.

This news rocked the country to its foundations. The nation was immediately split into two camps— those who denounced the execution of the king and saw in it a threat to all established governments, and those who accepted the execution as necessary for the success of the revolution in France. For a while and in the cities, the first group were in the majority. In Providence, Rhode Island, all the bells of the town were tolled in mourning for the French king. Fashionable ladies wore dark roses as a sign of mourning in New York and Philadelphia and others ordered wardrobes of black to portray their sympathies for the dead king.

Suddenly King Louis XVI became a martyr not only among the Hamiltonians but among many who had supported Jefferson and were strongly opposed to any form of monarchy. Jefferson was oddly the villain of the piece. "Jacobin," people hissed at him, and the term was as hateful as "Commie" two centuries later. Again the word went around that all this was the result of trusting in the philosophies of a madman like Tom Jefferson who believed that power belonged to the people. Give power to the people and only anarchy could result; the proof of that lay in France, said Jefferson's enemies.

Jefferson, still living in Philadelphia, found himself the loneliest man in the United States. There were, he told Madison, not more than three people in the whole town who were prepared to welcome him in their houses. Others, whom he had known for many years, passed him in the road without a word, or even crossed to the other side of the street to avoid him.

He was fond of company and now found himself a kind of pariah in the very city where he had written the Declaration of Independence. But his kind of independence, his kind of republicanism was not to be swayed by popular reaction. He would not alter his stand by as much as a scruple. Men were born free and had a right to govern themselves that was far greater than the so-called divine right of kings.

As a human being, he was deeply shocked that Louis XVI had been beheaded. As a champion of men's independence, he rejoiced that monarchs were "amenable to punishment like any other criminal." On his finger he had a signet ring on which was carved "Rebellion to Tyrants is Obedience to God." He looked often at the wording on that signet ring now. It was his motto and, cut off from all society in Philadelphia, he drew strength from it.

One other shared Jefferson's view on the execution of King Louis—his friend James Madison. As soon as he heard the news, Madison wrote to Jefferson about the execution, "If he was a traitor he ought to be punished like any other man." Madison was staunch then, and Jefferson drew a great deal of comfort from that.

When the popular emotion over the execution began to subside a little, the nation turned to examine another aspect of the news which had not escaped Jefferson from the start. That was that France was now at war with Britain and Spain. British Redcoats were prepared then to squash the French Revolution as at one time they had tried to squash the American Revolution. When the import of this news sank into the public mind, there was an abrupt change in the attitude of many.

They forgot about "Louis the Martyr" and their sympathies were entirely with the French, so much so that Jacobin Clubs which were really only pro-French clubs, were formed throughout the country, and the most popular song soon became the rousing "Marseillaise," which was roared out in taverns from Boston, Massachusetts to Boonesboro, Kentucky.

In the country among the small farmers, where Jefferson had his real support, the people had not been overly perturbed over the execution of Louis. Sympathy for the king and opposition to the French rebels was strongest in the cities among the merchant and manufacturing classes. The country people remembered the great help the French had given to the United States in its own period of revolt. Gratitude demanded that the United States aid France in its war against Great Britain.

The revolution in France was no longer just a matter of academic interest. Now that it was likely to be crushed by Britain in league with other European monarchies, it involved American interests directly.

If the Coalition of Kings, as it was called, crushed the French Republic, then surely the American Republic would be next on the list.

"To arms," shouted the French, singing the "Marseillaise."

"To arms," shouted many Americans, also singing the "Marseillaise."

Sitting under the plane trees that surrounded his house in Philadelphia, Thomas Jefferson heard the shout and was troubled. He was troubled for France and troubled for America—but mostly for America, the birthplace of freedom.

President Washington received the news that France was at war with Great Britain early in April while he was resting at Mount Vernon. He wrote immediately to Jefferson, warning him that the government must do everything possible to prevent the country being embroiled in the war. Then he journeyed immediately to Philadelphia and on April 19, 1793 called a fateful meeting of his cabinet.

The subject of the meeting was the war between Britain and France. The matter was one of the government's foreign policy and so belonged in Jefferson's department, but Hamilton had views of his own on what should be done, and he was no man to hold back for fear of trespass in another's affairs. His sympathies were pro-British and he believed that the United States should break off relations with Republican France.

"Our Treaty of Alliance with France, concluded in 1778, was concluded with King Louis XVI. The king has been beheaded. The treaty therefore can exist no more. The alliance is no longer binding."

Thomas Jefferson listened grimly and silently to Hamilton's arguments. They were precisely what he had expected and, when Hamilton had done, he beat them to the ground with the one tremendous weapon of which he was master—reason.

"The Secretary of the Treasury seems to hold the view that we enter into treaties with individuals," he said icily. "But this is not the case. Treaties are entered into between nations, and nations have the right to change their form of government without forfeiting their previous treaty arrangements. The Treaty of Alliance of 1778 was not concluded with an individual called Louis Capet who happened to be King of France, but with the French Government—the French State. And that government, though changed, still exists and the treaty must be honored. It is a treaty between two nations—America and France, and the individuals concerned in its signing have no bearing on the matter.

"Indeed I find it peculiar," he continued, "that we, a republic, should have no hesitation at all in concluding an alliance with a despotic king, but some gentlemen object to the same alliance being extended to a French republic. Would the Secretary of the Treasury never have agreed to an alliance with France in 1778 if France had been a republic at that time?"

Hamilton went white with anger, but he could make no reply. Too late he realized that he had stepped into an area in which he was no longer the authority. Washington and Attorney General Randolph agreed with Jefferson. The French Republic would have to be recognized. The Treaty of Alliance which had brought the French Army and Navy to the aid of American arms in the Revolutionary War, would have to be honored.

And yet there was a terrible danger. For, if the treaty were honored in full, the United States must open her ports to French vessels; must allow them to equip themselves in American harbors; must permit British prizes to be brought into American harbors. Inevitably the United States would be dragged into a war with Britain. And the country was too young and too weak to risk its newly won independence in a war on behalf of another, with little hope of winning.

There it was. The Treaty of Alliance had to be acknowledged. But the very acknowledgement would jeopardize the short-lived independence of the United States of America whose Army was equipped only for Indian fighting, and whose Navy was, in fact, non-existent.

"Let us recognize the Republic of France," said Jefferson. "Let us receive a French minister from the new republic if one is appointed. But let us warn the whole country that there must be no meddling by any of our citizens in this war."

This then was what the cabinet agreed. A proclamation was drawn up "forbidding the citizens of the United States to take part in any hostilities on the seas, and warning them against carrying to the belligerents any articles deemed contraband according to the modern usages of nations, and forbidding all acts and proceedings inconsistent with the duties of a friendly nation towards those at war."

This proclamation signed by President Washington and posted throughout the country was accepted by some but denounced as a "royal edict" by others. The rank and file of Americans, not aware of the grave issues at stake, were deeply grateful to France for its aid during the Revolutionary War. They wanted to pay off some of that debt of gratitude and thought it shameful to stand by while France battled Great Britain for her life. Furthermore, there was a fine profit to be made out of getting a commission as a privateer and raiding British shipping. Prize money would likely be fat, and the British Navy was too busy in Europe to protect British merchantmen in the West Indies.

Hard on the heels of that critical Cabinet meeting, Jefferson got a letter from Gouverneur Morris, the American Minister in France. It came by confidential hand and Jefferson took it immediately to the President, showing the contents to nobody else.

The letter announced that the new French Republic, as one of its first acts, had appointed "Citizen Edmond Charles Genêt" Minister to the United States. Genêt had secretly been given three hundred blank commissions to be issued to American privateers to prey on British shipping. "They suppose," wrote Morris, "that the avidity of some adventurers may lead them into measures which would involve altercations with Great Britain, and terminate finally in war."

"You know this man Genêt?" asked Washington.

"Only very slightly," said Jefferson. "We have not met but he was in the French Foreign Ministry under the old Count Vergennes when Dr. Franklin was our Minister to Paris. His sister was, I believe, a lady in waiting to Queen Marie Antoinette."

"Hmmm," said Washington. "He is one of the aristocrats?"

"Yes," said Jefferson.

"An aristocrat who has suddenly become a citizen?" said Washington. "I suppose he knows which side his bread is buttered on," he said grimly.

"Don't misjudge him," said Jefferson. "He is not an opportunist. There are, as you know, many French aristocrats who are republicans at heart. Genêt is not to be judged by his noble birth but rather by what he has done himself for the good of his people. The new French Republic obviously needs men trained in diplomacy and I would venture a guess that although born to a title, Citizen Genêt, as he is now called, is a true republican at heart."

"Well, we shall have to receive him," said Washington. "But he will have to be kept at a distance. Plainly his whole mission will be, using the Treaty of Alliance, to bring us gradually but inevitably into the war on the side of France. And that we must never allow him to do. That is your department, sir. I know you will be circumspect in your commitments and conversations with him."

Jefferson nodded. In the service of the United States he must now do something, for the safety of his country and its continued independence, which he would never do as a private individual. He must find some way of avoiding an obligation. Where other Americans, following the revolution, had refused to pay their debts to British merchants, Jefferson had paid every penny even though the payment came close to ruining him.

And now there was a debt of gratitude to be paid to

France which the country could not afford to pay, and he must find some method of avoiding the payment.

He agreed that the debt to France could not be paid. There was not one hair of difference on this question between himself and the President. The United States could not afford war with Britain. Yet the avoidance of that debt ran contrary to his personal sense of honor and, not for the first time, Jefferson found himself heartily hating the business of public service.

When he left the President's room and walked through the streets, he was no longer avoided or ignored. People crossed the street to meet him, to wish him "Good day," to give him their good wishes. Some of them were wearing the red bonnets which were the badge of republican France and they looked to him as the friend of France and so their hero. He saw the French tricolor on some buildings and horsemen wearing a French cockade in their hats.

What was he, then—a defender of liberty? Or did he limit his defense of liberty to liberty in America? But was not liberty indivisible and would not the crushing of liberty in France portend the crushing of liberty in the United States? After all, it was his belief that all men, not just Americans, were endowed with certain natural rights and foremost among them was the right to govern themselves.

The solution of the problem was painful, slow but sure. America was the birthplace of the new kind of liberty that recognized all men as having equal rights. Well, if it were not actually the birthplace (for the idea had come from the writings of many Europeans) then it was the place where these ideas had been incorporated in a Constitution. Therefore it was essential that America survive. To survive, she must mind her own business and not get involved in the quarrels of others. Neutrality in the wars of others should be the American policy. The great conquests were achieved not on the battlefield but in the minds of men, and liberty would grow not as the result of the roar of cannons but as the result of the noiseless impact of written words.

The results of the Revolution could not be jeopardized or thrown away in order gallantly to satisfy a debt to France. Perhaps Citizen Genêt would understand. He would have to judge how much of his heart to lay bare to the man after he had met him. These were the conclusions which Jefferson made and in reaching them he lay down a precept for American policy for generations to come. That precept was that in the wars of other nations America should always observe a strict neutrality.

Citizen Genêt, when he arrived in the United States, was but thirty years of age—and a flaming republican. When he was only twenty-five he had been sent to the court of Catherine of Russia and there his outspoken views against despotism and privilege resulted in his being asked to leave the country. That was enough to recommend him to the French authorities who sent him with high hopes as their minister to republican America.

Genêt was a man of many talents. He could speak several languages fluently, and had translated a small Swedish book when he was twelve years of age. He had a quick mind, an eloquent tongue and plenty of personal dash and charm. But the one talent he had not got was the one essential to his office. He was completely lacking in prudence and expected on arrival to be the hero of the nation and to receive every aid of which France stood in need.

He was certainly the hero of the nation. He arrived in Charleston, South Carolina on a French frigate and was met by a reception that would have turned the head of a man twice his years. The docks were strung with French bunting, the streets thick with a cheering multitude all of whose sympathies lay with France. Indeed, had he been landing in a French city after performing some great service for his country, he would not have been greeted with more enthusiasm.

His journey overland from Charleston to Philadelphia occupied a month and was, in essence, a triumphal procession. At every town and hamlet he entered, he was given an official welcome. There were banners and speeches and flags hung across the streets, and people pressed around his carriage to get a glimpse of him and perhaps have the privilege of touching him.

The newspapers throughout the country, except the Federalist press, formed a chorus of praise for France and its young ambassador, and Jefferson was delighted to find the "old spirit of '76 rekindling the newspapers from Boston to Charleston" and forcing "the monocrat papers . . . to publish the most furious philippics against England."

It seemed to Jefferson, who was constantly concerned that some kind of monarchy would be established in the United States, that the arrival of Genêt had brought the people to their senses. Even Madison, the soberest judge of events, was happy at the spontaneous enthusiasm for republicanism that showed everywhere Genêt went.

Yet Jefferson was aware that there was some danger in this enthusiasm, too. He did not want the people in their zeal for Genêt to push the country into war with Britain by some reckless act. He did not want some Charleston privateer to seize a British ship and thus provide Britain with an excuse for declaring war on the United States. Washington, who of course shared these fears, agreed that the official reception of Genêt would be cordial but not overly warm.

When Genêt arrived in Philadelphia, his reception was even greater than it had been elsewhere. Every civic and social group passed resolutions of welcome and presented them to him. He was invited to a vast republican banquet as guest of honor and the whole assembly at the banquet rose to sing "La Marseillaise." Indeed, so great were the private and unofficial welcomes for Genêt that he was two days in Philadelphia before he was able to present his credentials to President Washington and receive his formal welcome into the country.

Washington, despite the fact that Genêt had now been in the country six weeks without presenting his credentials, received him warmly and expressed his sincere regard for the French nation. Genêt, bubbling with enthusiasm, all but embraced Washington and told Jefferson, "We see in you the only person on earth who can love us sincerely and merit to be so loved."

Genêt's sincerity touched Jefferson but he was worried about the young Frenchman's ardor and utter lack of prudence. He thought that perhaps he would be able to advise Genêt on how to conduct himself, suggest that it was not the wisest thing to be making public addresses to the people of the United States before he had presented his credentials to the President of the United States. In fact, it was not the part of the foreign minister to make public addresses at any time.

But Genêt was not the kind of a man who would listen to advice. He brought enthusiasm for the Republican cause, and right on the heels of it he raised so many problems that he nearly wrecked the Republican cause in the United States.

While he was in Charleston, before even being officially received as minister, he gave out some of the privateering commissions to Charleston shipowners. These commissions were a license to the shipowners to seize British vessels, not as pirates, but as agents fighting on behalf of France. The place of the privateer in war was well recognized in those days, but Genêt had no right to issue such commissions without having presented his credentials. Particularly had he no right to issue them when President Washington had made a proclamation calling on all Americans to remain strictly neutral in the conflict. Genêt was hardly in the United States, then, before he was ignoring and encouraging American citizens to ignore the President's proclamation.

It was not long before this foolhardiness, this highhanded attitude towards President Washington, bore bitter fruit. Privateers fitted out in Charleston began bringing back British prizes. And worse still, a French privateer captured a British merchantman, *The Little Sarah*, in American coastal waters and brought her as a prize into Philadelphia. There Genêt announced she would be outfitted and armed to become a war vessel of France. She would be given the name of *Le Petit Democrat* (The Little Democrat) and sent to sea with a crew of Americans, bearing a commission issued by France.

There was an immediate and angry protest from the British minister in Philadelphia. The vessel had been in American waters, which were neutral waters, and therefore should not have been attacked in the first place, he said. Secondly, she should not have been brought into an American port since America proclaimed neutrality. Thirdly, it was against all the laws of nations that America should allow the ship to be re-equipped as a war vessel in an American port. That was not neutrality, the British minister said. That was war—and war on the side of France.

The seizure of *The Little Sarah* occurred while Washington had gone to Mount Vernon to attend to pressing private affairs there. General Mifflin, Governor of Pennsylvania, sent his secretary to Genêt to persuade him to order the vessel to remain in Philadelphia until President Washington had returned to the city.

Genêt high-handedly said he would do nothing of the sort. The ship would go to sea as soon as ready. Mifflin's secretary replied politely that if the minister would not agree to detail the vessel, then the Governor would have to keep it in Philadelphia by force.

At this Genêt flew into a rage. "You have no right to do any such thing," he stormed. "You are like all the officials of this country. You treat me, the representative of republican France, coldly while your own people applaud and support me. Why should I keep this ship in Philadelphia until President Washington returns? Who is President Washington? Is he the king of America? Does he give orders and everybody has to obey them?

"I tell you that President Washington has no right to order the governors of states, such as your master, to stop a French vessel leaving an American port. Only the Congress could give him such authority and the Congress has not done so. Your President is exceeding his powers. I will go directly to the people of America over this issue and if any attempt is made to seize this vessel, it will be repelled with force."

Mr. Dallas, Governor Mifflin's secretary, sat through this tirade angrily and then reported the interview to the Governor. The Governor replied by ordering out one hundred and twenty militia to seize the privateer. He also sent a message to Jefferson detailing the situation.

Jefferson went immediately to Genêt and repeated the request that *The Little Sarah* should not sail until President Washington returned to Philadelphia.

"You are aware," he said, "that President Washington has proclaimed our neutrality and that a proclamation has forbidden American citizens from engaging in any hostile acts against any nation—England or France. You have Americans on board your vessel, it has been equipped for war in an American port. This is a direct breach—"

That was as far as the fiery Frenchman would let Jefferson go. He thrust his chair back and was on his feet in an instant, striding up and down his office, shaking his finger at Jefferson. Jefferson found the performance faintly amusing.

"The United States has violated its Treaty of Alliance with France," he stormed. "It has permitted its own flag to be dishonored, for American ships have been stopped by British vessels on the high seas and cargoes destined for France have been removed from them. The United States has done nothing to prevent this. Now the United States is stopping French vessels from putting to sea from American ports.

"Ever since I have been in this country [he had not been there very long] I have been thwarted by the ministers of the country whom I looked upon as my friends. I have been thwarted by President Washington and by you and by every official of the government I have come in contact with. Not merely thwarted. Opposed. Yes, sir. Prevented from doing those things for my country for which I was sent here. I have often thought of packing and taking the next available ship back to France for there is nothing useful I can do for my nation in a country whose highest officials are anti-French. . . ."

"One moment, sir . . ." said Jefferson.

"No," cried Genêt. "I will not hear you. You must hear me. You are in the wrong and your President is in the wrong and violating the trust given to him by the people of the United States. He is taking to himself powers that belong to the Congress. He had no right to proclaim neutrality without the consent of the Congress. When he returns to Philadelphia I will demand that he convene the Congress and then this matter will be aired before that body."

So Genêt stormed on, and Jefferson who had many years before learned to control his own temper listened patiently and waited for the end of the tirade.

When Genêt got to the subject of the Congress,

Jefferson raised his hand and stopped the Frenchman. "My good sir," he said, "you complain of having been thwarted by the officials of the government. But I now perceive at last the source of all your vexations."

"What is it?" cried Genêt.

"You are a minister to our country, but you have made the mistake of not studying our Constitution," said Jefferson calmly. "You think that all the authority of our government is lodged in one body, the Congress. But you are quite wrong. Our government has three authorities, each sovereign in its own field. They are the executive, the legislative and the judiciary. All the questions which you raise are not the concern of the Congress, the legislative body. They are the concern of the executive body—the President and his ministers of whom I am one."

"Do you mean to tell me," said Genêt, "that the Congress of the United States is not the sovereign body of this republic?"

"That is precisely what I mean to tell you," said Jefferson. "The Congress is sovereign only in making laws, the executive is sovereign in carrying out the laws, and the judiciary is sovereign in construing the laws—that is in interpreting them and in some cases deciding whether the laws are constitutional or not."

"But surely," Genêt objected, "Congress is bound to see that the treaties entered into by the United States are observed?"

"Not at all," said Jefferson. "The Congress has very limited powers with regard to the observance of treaties. It is the duty of the President to ensure that the nation's treaty obligations are observed."

"But if your President decides against honoring the provisions of a treaty, to whom can an appeal be addressed?" demanded Genêt.

"The Constitution provides that there is no appeal from the President's decision," said Jefferson. "The President is the last appeal."

Genêt stared at Jefferson, thunderstruck. Then he collected himself, shrugged and made a stiff bow. "I cannot compliment you, sir," he said, "upon your Constitution."

"It is perhaps not a perfect instrument, being devised by men," said Jefferson, "yet it is the best of any of which I have knowledge and I assure you, sir, that I have studied the subject thoroughly. Your problem concerns the President of the United States and not the Congress of the United States. You say that the detaining of the vessel *The Little Sarah* in Philadelphia is a violation of our treaty with France. I tell you that whether it is a violation or not—and I do not think it is—must be decided by the President.

"Therefore I ask you to issue orders to prevent the vessel's sailing until President Washington has returned here from Mount Vernon. If you permit her to sail before the President returns, I must warn you that you will have committed a very grave offense against the United States indeed."

"The problem does not arise in any case," said Genêt. "You say President Washington will be here in a few days. The vessel is not in a state of readiness to sail."

"I have been informed on good authority that she is to be moved out of Philadelphia," said Jefferson.

"Yes, but only a few miles," said Genêt. "She has some stores to take aboard at Chester. I repeat that she is not ready to sail."

"Will you promise that she will not sail until President Washington has had an opportunity to consider the matter?" Jefferson persisted.

But Genêt would give no such promise. Such a promise he said was unnecessary. She wasn't ready for sea and would not be ready for sea for several days. And then, with a return to his previous lack of prudence he said, "I beseech you not to permit any attempt to put men on board of her. She is filled with high-spirited patriots and they will unquestionably resist. And there is no occasion, for I tell you she will not be ready to depart for some time."

Jefferson then left having arrived at two conclusions. The first was that the privateer would remain in the river and so there was no need for the militia to seize her. The second was that Citizen Genêt was too impetuous a man to represent France in the United States. He was more than impetuous. He was impertinent and ignorant and pigheaded and would not hesitate to interfere in the domestic affairs of the United States.

Regarding the first of these conclusions, Jefferson sent a message to Governor Mifflin saying that he was assured that *The Little Sarah* could not leave for several days and therefore it was not necessary that she be seized by the militia.

Regarding the second conclusion, Jefferson decided that Citizen Genêt must be recalled to France. The trick was to achieve this without giving offense to the French government.

☆ **11** ☆

Alexander Hamilton had heard of the capture of *The Little Sarah* by the French privateer even before the news reached Secretary of State Thomas Jefferson. Hamilton had been told of the capture by Hammond, the British minister in Philadelphia with whom he was in close contact.

When Jefferson discovered that Hamilton had received the news first and had got it from the British minister, his anger against the Secretary of the Treasury increased. He believed that Hamilton was passing on to the British many details of government policy and activity which, if they were to be revealed at all, should be revealed by him.

He further believed that Hamilton, through his connection with the British minister, was undercutting his work as Secretary of State. Hamilton, he concluded, wished to run not merely the Treasury but also the foreign department. In fact, he wanted to run the whole country. And Hamilton had Washington's confidence. His own influence with Washington, he felt, was slight and diminishing.

The crisis precipitated by Genêt and *The Little Sarah* remained in abeyance for but a day or two. Jefferson wrote a full report of the matter for Washington and sent it to his office, marked "For instant attention." He came down with a bout of fever and had to go to bed. While he was in bed with fever, Washington returned from Mount Vernon to find the problem of *The Little Sarah*, with the grave threat of war with Great Britain if the ship was permitted to sail, confronting him.

Washington was in a bad humor. It seemed to him that every time he left Philadelphia to visit his home some calamity arose and his two squabbling ministers were unable to solve it. There had been a number of articles in the newspapers, notably in the *Gazette* published by Freneau, criticizing him, and one particularly ugly attack, likening him to a despot. Freneau completely sided with Genêt, embarrassing Jefferson as much as Washington, but Jefferson refused to interfere with him, believing in complete freedom for the press.

He would not even discharge him from his job as translation clerk in the State Department, though Freneau's devotion to Genêt jeopardized his own policies. Even when Washington asked him to use his influence to get Freneau to tone down his attitude, Jefferson refused to do so. He believed in the right of people to express their views, however distasteful, and would not disturb that right.

Washington then, in a black mood, read Jefferson's

report on *The Little Sarah* incident, and sent a curt note to Jefferson.

"What is to be done in the case of *The Little Sarah* now at Chester?" he demanded. "Is the minister of the French Republic to set the acts of this government at defiance with impunity? And threaten the executive with an appeal to the people? [For Jefferson had included a report of this threat in the papers he left for Washington to read.] What must the world think of such conduct and of the government of the United States in submitting to it?

"These are serious questions. Circumstances press for decision and, as you have had time to consider them (upon me they come unexpectedly), I wish to know your opinion upon them, even before tomorrow, for the vessel may then be gone."

Jefferson had never before received such a note from Washington. It implied a sharp reprimand, as if he had in some way been neglecting the duties of his office. He had included in his report to Washington his recommendations about what should be done. In bed with fever he got pen and paper and wrote a short note to the President, to be taken to him immediately. It read: "T.J. is of himself of opinion that whatever is aboard of her of arms, ammunition, or men, contrary to the rules heretofore laid down by the President, ought to be withdrawn."

The next day, Jefferson, still ill, mounted his horse and rode into downtown Philadelphia for a meeting of the cabinet on the subject. It was a brief meeting, with Hamilton playing on the fear of war with Britain and Jefferson struggling to preserve American neutrality towards all combatants. Jefferson finally won the point that all privateers, British or French, in American ports should be seized. Hamilton did not mind seizing French privateers. But to seize British privateers would bring down on the country the whole might of the British Navy.

"We cannot have one-sided neutrality," said Jefferson. His point of view prevailed. Genêt was informed of the decision to detain all privateers which had been outfitting in American ports.

But Citizen Genêt had no intention of obeying the laws of the country to which he had been appointed minister. He ordered *The Little Sarah,* now *Le Petit Democrat,* to sea. Both Washington and Jefferson were defied and the nation cheered the Frenchman. A stranger might have concluded that Americans thought more of Genêt than they did of their own President or Secretary of State. Genêt was a stranger and he certainly came to that conclusion. He was sure he had more influence with the people of the United States than either Washington or Jefferson and this conviction led him to plunge even more boldly into meddling with the country's affairs.

His first step was to form a Democratic Society of people who were devoted to the French cause in the war with Britain. Soon there were dozens of Democratic clubs throughout the States, all of them ultra-Republican. These clubs agitated for a war with Britain on the side of France. Then Genêt started writing articles for the Republican papers, including that published by Freneau, advocating the French cause and reminding Americans of the great debt they owed to France.

He had already issued privateering commissions to American captains in defiance of the President's proclamation of neutrality. He now issued commissions to frontiersmen in Kentucky and other states to take up arms against the British on the western frontier. In short, he did everything possible to drag the United States into war with Britain.

"Genêt must go," Jefferson told Madison in one of their talks at his Philadelphia home. "His unwarrantable meddling is an immediate danger to the country. Furthermore, he is utterly destroying the Republican cause in the nation. It is widely assumed that as a friend of France I support Genêt and the Federalists are making the most of the situation."

This was true. It was not hard for clever writers in the Federalist papers to imply that Jefferson, the friend of France, was an apostle of anarchy and bent on war with Britain, and against these accusations he had no defense, for he would write no articles himself. Freneau, as noted, entirely agreed with Genêt and wrote article after article advocating war. And Jefferson refused to silence him though these articles hurt his own policies and position.

Madison most of this time was in Virginia, visiting Philadelphia only occasionally, but realizing the damage that Genêt was doing to Jefferson's party, the Democratic-Republicans, he prepared a resolution divorcing Jefferson and his party both from Genêt and from the excesses of the French Revolution. Copies of this resolution were sent to various centers, adopted at party meetings and news of the adoption rushed to the papers for printing. Then another blow fell.

Gideon Hanfield, an American citizen, was arrested

in Charleston for having enlisted on a French privateer contrary to Washington's proclamation of neutrality. He was hardly arrested before the extremists of the Republican Party made him a hero. Hanfield was brought into court and pleaded that he had enlisted before the President's neutrality proclamation. In his defense he asked the court whether it was indeed a crime for an American to volunteer to fight for France, America's old ally, against despotic King George III of Great Britain?

Hanfield was acquitted and carried in triumph through the streets of Charleston. The acquittal, since Hanfield had enlisted before the proclamation prohibiting enlistments, was justified. But the public reaction in making a hero of Hanfield, put the President in an extremely bad light and further inflated Genêt's ego. He wrote to a friend that "old Washington" was jealous of his popularity in America.

Jefferson had given a great deal of thought to Genêt's position and how to arrange for his recall. He did not want to offend France by demanding the recall of its minister. He certainly did not want to go to the extreme of breaking diplomatic relations with the French Republic. On August 1, 1793, Washington took the matter into his own hands and called a meeting of his cabinet to discuss the question.

The whole of Genêt's correspondence with the government, with Washington, with Jefferson and with Hamilton, was reviewed and the cabinet agreed unanimously that he must go. Hamilton argued for direct and immediate action. "Withdraw his credentials and send him packing," he said. "He has outrageously exceeded all the privileges granted to a foreign envoy."

"Such a course would not do," said Jefferson. "We must be sure that in getting rid of an individual we do not injure a nation. I am quite sure that M. Genêt has exceeded his instructions and if this is pointed out to the French government, through our own ambassador, he will be recalled by the French government. Not discharged by ourselves."

Secretary of War Knox, who almost invariably sided with Hamilton, wanted Genêt thrown out without any nicety, which would be pleasing to the British, whose friendship he wished to court. But Jefferson would not countenance any such procedure.

"The request for a minister's withdrawal should not be made into an affront to a whole nation," he reiterated.

"Request?" cried Hamilton. "We have only to dismiss him—to withdraw his credentials. We do not have to make a request at all."

"I am aware," said Jefferson quietly, "that there are some among us who have no sympathy whatever with the French Republic and hold everything they do obnoxious. But in dealing with other nations the question is not where one's individual sympathies lie but what is best for our own nation. Individual viewpoints must not be allowed to influence national policies.

"Let us assume for a moment that it was not M. Genêt the French ambassador who had offended us, but Mr. Hammond, the British ambassador. Would the gentlemen then be so anxious to get rid of Mr. Hammond—to withdraw *his* credentials and throw *him* out and risk breaking our diplomatic relations with Great Britain and indeed incurring the wrath of that country?"

To this Hamilton had no reply.

In these cabinet meetings, Washington normally spoke very little. Indeed there were many of them during which he said nothing while Hamilton and Jefferson fought out the issue. Then, and then only, he would make his decision. Despite the fact that he had been personally affronted by Genêt, and his position as President of the United States belittled by the imprudent French minister, he took no sides in the debate, or rather argument between his two ministers, but when they had done he ruled quietly that Jefferson was in the right. A full report on Genêt should be transmitted to the French government through the American minister in Paris, Gouverneur Morris. It should be accompanied by copies of all relevant correspondence and the French government should be asked to recall Genêt.

Hamilton then brought up the matter of the public reaction in America to Genêt's recall. "The man is a hero to many of our citizens," he said. "People are going to question why he was recalled. I propose that the whole of his correspondence be published together with a statement of the proceedings here, in the form of an appeal to the people for support."

Jefferson was appalled. Publish official and confidential documents in the press? Put before the public the whole story of the heated cabinet debate on Genêt with Hamilton demanding ejection and Jefferson arguing for a more diplomatic approach? This would only publicize and widen the split in the government.

"Unthinkable," he said. "The government is entitled to ask for the recall of any foreign minister without appealing to the people to support the action."

"Perhaps so," said Hamilton, "but our good Republican friend Mr. Genêt has such a grasp of the public fancy that there will be an uproar over his recall unless the government presents its case clearly to the people."

"The course you propose," said Jefferson, "would bring an immediate answer from Genêt. He would rush into print with his side of the story also, in an appeal for popular support. There will then be a contest between the President and Genêt in the public press. You may be sure that anonymous writers will take the matter up. There would be the same difference of opinion in public as there is here in this cabinet. Congress, you may be assured, will then take up the matter, dividing on one side and the other. Nothing but bickering and acrimony can result from such a course at home and can you imagine what would be the reaction abroad—the President of the United States and the former French ambassador arguing their case in the weekly papers?"

Secretary of War Knox now blundered into the discussion. A great fighter in the Revolutionary War when he had been in charge of the Continental artillery, he was no diplomat.

"The President has already been subjected to intolerable abuse in the press," he said. He produced a newspaper in which there was a cartoon entitled, "Funeral of George Washington." It showed Washington on the guillotine, about to be beheaded like the late king of France. The inference was that Washington was as much of a despot as Louis XVI.

When he saw this cartoon, Washington flew into an uncontrollable rage. Turning on Jefferson, he denounced the personal abuse that had been heaped on him. "I defy any man, here or in any part of the nation, to produce a single act of mine that has not been performed in the interest of the country," he thundered. "Before God, I would rather be in my grave than occupy my present office. I would rather be on my farm than emperor of the whole world. And yet, here are the people charging me with wanting to be a king."

These rages of Washington's were rare. But when they occurred, his voice was thunderous, his face red with passion and no one dared to utter a word until his anger was spent.

Thumping his fist on the table, Washington said he repented every moment that had passed since he agreed to run for a second term.

"Want to be king?" he cried. "I am sick of the charge; sick of those who hint it and sick of those who deny it. I have given the whole of my manhood to the service of the country and as a reward am held up to the ridicule and scorn of the nation."

So he went on, and when his anger had run out, there was complete silence. Then Washington said quietly, "It is agreed that the Secretary of State shall write to our Minister in Paris asking him to request the recall of Genêt. When that has been done we will see what the public reaction is and whether it is necessary to publish any of the papers in the case to justify ourselves."

That closed the cabinet meeting. Genêt was to go. But as matters turned out, Secretary of State Jefferson was to go, too.

☆ **12** ☆

The day before that critical cabinet meeting on the subject of M. Genêt, Thomas Jefferson had written the President a letter of resignation. He had been thinking about his position for many weeks during the furor over Genêt. The position seemed to him to be intolerable and he decided that someone else, more competent than he, should take over the duties of Secretary of State.

For one thing, he could not shake off the conviction that Hamilton, with the support of Vice-President John Adams, was intent upon gradually changing the Republic of the United States into a monarchic form of government. He spoke about this many times to Washington, and Washington each time denied that there was any such move anywhere in the government. On this crucial matter, then, Washington did not believe him.

Again, Washington had asked him to put an end to Freneau's attacks on himself, the President, and on the government. Jefferson, because he believed in freedom of the press, could not agree to do this. Lastly, in the business of maintaining strict neutrality in the war between Britain and France, he was, he believed, being obstructed by Hamilton who wanted to adopt a policy that favored Britain over France.

There was not a single area of his work in which he could make any progress, let alone hold his ground. So he wrote his letter to Washington, asking leave to retire at the end of September—in two months time.

Washington called immediately on Jefferson and the two of them threshed the matter out in the shade of the plane trees by the bank of the river.

"I cannot adequately convey to you my distress at your desire to resign," said Washington. "The whole country is in an uproar over this French business. I looked to you to counsel me and if you are not there, to whom am I to turn? I can find no one who will adequately replace you as Secretary of State."

"And yet," said Jefferson, "I can be only an inefficient Secretary of State and any substitute would do better than I."

"You are not offended over the recent cabinet meeting?" asked Washington anxiously.

"No, sir," said Jefferson. "You have been under villainous attack and I have admired your forebearance. You know my devotion to you. There is no question of any animosity between the two of us."

"Then why your resignation at this critical time?" asked Washington.

"I am sorry to have to go over this painful ground again," said Jefferson, "but perhaps I can put all in a plain light so that you will see that my resignation is the only proper action left to me. I cannot, without compromising my principles concerning freedom of the press, put any pressure on Freneau or any other editor to cease their attacks on you and your administration. Those attacks are as painful to me as they are to you. Yet I must endure them and must stand by and see you suffer from them. It is no spectacle for the country to see the President attacked by a man who earns a salary in the office of the Secretary of State. I cannot discharge Freneau. The only honorable thing to do is to resign myself."

"But surely I am not to be deprived of your talents . . ." interrupted Washington.

"You have heard only one reason for my resignation," said Jefferson. "I pray you to listen to the others. As your Secretary of State I am obliged to move and mix among people who resent my Republican views and bear me particular hatred. No word I write, no chance remark I make is not seized upon, distorted, published in distorted form and sent throughout the nation not merely to injure me but to injure those principles for which I stand. I am powerless to combat these calumnies which come from the drawing rooms of the wealthy, from merchants whose whole business is dependent on trade with England, and from those who have made fortunes in paper money with stock speculation.

"Finally, you are fully aware of the hostility which exists between myself and Mr. Hamilton. It has gone beyond the stage of any compromise. Our views are entirely opposed one to the other and this kind of division in your cabinet, is the worst possible state of affairs for the nation. We are set at each other like two cocks in a pit.

"'That, sir, is not government. It is mere tavern argument. I respect Mr. Hamilton's personal integrity as I respect my own. But I abominate his principles as he abominates mine. There is not one inch of common ground on which we can meet. For better or for worse I have become the leader of the Republican cause; Mr. Hamilton the leader of the monarchists or Federalists, which is the term he prefers. Two such horses cannot work together in harness."

"You have warned me a great deal about monarchy," said Washington. "But I assure you that there is not a man in the United States who would set his face more decidedly against such a change than myself."

"No rational man suspects you of any other disposition," asserted Jefferson, "but not a week goes by in which I could not produce declarations dropping from the monarchical party that our government is good for nothing, is a milk and water thing that cannot support itself, that we must knock it down and set up something with more energy."

"If that is so," said Washington, "then it is proof of their insanity, for the republican spirit of the Union is so clear and solid that it is astonishing how anyone could expect to move it."

Washington then turned to the radical republicans who were agitating for war on the side of France and had the country in a turmoil over the question, rallying behind Genêt.

"They will soon desert Genêt when they know the truth about him," said Jefferson. "And the truth will come out. It is not something that can be hidden."

"I don't doubt the loyalty of the Republican Party,"

said the President, "but when men put a machine into motion it is impossible to stop it exactly where they choose, or even to say where it will stop. The agitation for war may make war. That is the danger in which we stand. And standing in that danger, I would ask you to consider your decision to resign."

But Jefferson had made up his mind and the President could not shake it.

"I have always disliked public office," he said. "There are others who have a talent for it, but I have none. The demand for compromise is beyond my capabilities. And added to this I have been in the public service now for twenty-five years and out of those years have scarcely had one full year at a time in my own home. My estates are run down; my private debts are mounting beyond my ability to pay them. My heart is not in Philadelphia but at Monticello, and that being so, it would be better for the country if I were replaced."

In the end Jefferson agreed to a compromise. He would continue in office until the fall when he would take a temporary leave of absence and return to his duties on January of the following year.

The President's insistence that Jefferson take merely a leave of absence was proof that Washington did not regard him in the same light as Hamilton did—the leader of a rabble which, if it gained power would lead the nation into anarchy. Jefferson's place was to be taken by Edmund Randolph, but there was still some work for Jefferson to do before he could return to Monticello.

Thomas Jefferson was incapable of doing anything behind anyone's back. The cabinet having agreed that

Genêt was to be recalled, he wrote the necessary letters to Morris in Paris and then decided that decency demanded that he inform Genêt that the United States government had written to his superiors, requesting his recall.

Genêt, while his fate was being debated in the cabinet, had gone to New York which was at the moment wildly enthusiastic about the French cause. The frigate *Ambuscade* which had brought Genêt to America, while at anchor in New York Harbor, had been challenged to combat by the British frigate *Boston*, under the command of Captain Courtney. The *Ambuscade* accepted the challenge and in the ship-to-ship duel which followed Courtney was killed and his frigate, heavily damaged, had to retreat to Halifax.

On the same day, a French fleet of fifteen ships arrived in the Hudson River from the Chesapeake. French seamen and officers swarmed through the city and New Yorkers cheered the French Republic, wore tri-color cockades and ribbons and every tavern in the city echoed choruses of the "Marseillaise."

When Genêt arrived there, he was the hero of the day. He came by water and landed at the Powles Hook Ferry in lower Manhattan to be met by a huge committee of officials. He was escorted through the streets amidst the deafening cheers of the people. Addresses were made to him in which he was assured that "the cause of France is the cause of America." He decided that Washington was wrong and he was right.

Washington had proclaimed American neutrality but the people wanted war on behalf of their ally, France. French flags flew from housetops beside the

American flag, and ribbons of red, white and blue were hung from almost every window. In any difficulty with Washington, then, he had only to put the facts before these splendid pro-French Americans and they would ignore the President and give him their full support.

While Genêt was basking in these rosy thoughts, he got a letter from Jefferson informing him that the United States government had requested his recall and courteously enclosing a copy of the letter Jefferson had written to Gouverneur Morris in Paris asking that this be done.

Genêt dashed off an angry reply, accusing Jefferson, Washington and everybody else he had come into contact with, of betraying him. He said that plainly America wanted only an ambassador from the French aristocracy, and not a representative of the new French Republic. He accused Washington of being sympathetic to Louis XVI, noting that when he had first met the President in Philadelphia, a portrait of Louis XVI and his Queen, Marie Antoinette, hung on the walls of Washington's office.

"There is an act of justice which the American people, which the French people, which all free people are interested in demanding," he concluded. "It is that a particular inquiry should be made, in the approaching Congress, into the motives which have induced the chief of the executive power of the United States to take upon himself to demand the recall of a public minister, whom the sovereign people of the United States have received fraternally and recognized."

That was Genêt's challenge. Americans loved him.

Washington disliked him. The American Congress should decide who was right.

Within a matter of days, the fact that Genêt had appealed to the Congress over the head of the President leaked out. Attempts were made at first to deny that this was so, but the rumor was finally confirmed.

Then Genêt witnessed an astonishing public change. His high-handedness was denounced in meetings held in almost every state of the Union. Washington's neutrality proclamation might not be popular, but Washington's powers as President had the fullest public support. Genêt sent a report of his case, with a demand that it be presented to the Congress, to Jefferson, and Jefferson handed the papers to Washington.

"I am giving you this demand of Genêt's for a congressional inquiry as a matter of form," he told the President. "But I have already told Genêt not once but many times that there is no appeal from the President's decision in such affairs."

"Send it back to him with the same reply," said the President.

So Jefferson wrote Genêt, telling him that as a foreign minister he could deal only with the President and not with the Congress. The letter was written on December 31, 1793, and it was Jefferson's last act as Secretary of State. He had postponed his temporary retirement at Washington's request to the very end of the year. He now wrote resigning his office, not for a temporary period but for good.

Washington reluctantly accepted the resignation and Thomas Jefferson packed his belongings and left Philadelphia.

The conclusion of Genêt's story is soon told. His own government recalled him, and a new minister arrived with instructions to arrest Genêt and send him back to France for trial.

Each day the guillotine in Paris was taking its terrible toll of human lives. Hundreds were decapitated between dawn and dusk to the cheers of the mob which now dominated the government of France. Genêt feared that if he were sent back to France he would be tried, condemned out of hand, and sent to the guillotine.

He appealed to Washington for permission to remain in the United States. Washington readily agreed. He would not hear of Genêt being sent back to France to certain death.

The reckless, outrageous French Foreign Minister, who had helped bring about the resignation of Thomas Jefferson, who had heavily damaged Jefferson's policies and challenged the authority of the President, became a political refugee in the United States.

He did well for himself. He married the daughter of Governor Clinton of New York, became a United States citizen, and lived out the rest of his life in peace and prosperity. There are indications that when he was able to vote, he voted for Jefferson's Republicans.

☆ 13 ☆

While Jefferson had been living in Philadelphia his expenses had exceeded his salary from the government by a hundred dollars a month. He kept a good staff in his house by the river—four or five servants headed by Petit, a steward and chef he brought over from France. A man of his position had to have a big establishment and had to be prepared to entertain foreign visitors of any importance.

Jefferson was also obliged to entertain all of his many friends who might be visiting Philadelphia. There was a stream of these visitors and he could refuse none of them. So his expenses were heavy and added to this he suffered all his life from an inability to resist buying books, pictures, scientific instruments and other articles which fascinated him. Also he had two daughters whom he loved dearly, and they, living in the country at Monticello, asked him now and then to get cloth for dresses or a particular bonnet which they heard was now the fashion.

Thomas Jefferson, in the midst of the furor over

Genêt and the attacks on his character and his principles, his quarrels with Hamilton and his talks with Washington—not to mention his work in inspecting inventions to decide whether a patent should be issued—in the midst then of all this business, went on shopping expeditions for Martha and Polly and for his little granddaughter who had been named Anne.

Martha wanted a kind of bonnet, called a calash, which was stretched over the head with hoops. Jefferson hunted around and found her one. Polly, who had finally got through *Don Quixote,* was rewarded with a particular kind of veil to be worn over a hat, and Jefferson had the milliner who sold it to him demonstrate how the veil was to be tied. He wrote Polly full details on wearing the veil with the precision with which he sent instructions to the country's ministers abroad.

"Observe that one of the strings is to be drawn tight around the root of the crown of the hat, and the veil then falling over the brim of the hat, is drawn by the lower string as tight or loose as you please around the neck," he wrote. "When the veil is not chosen to be drawn, the lower string is also tied around the root of the crown, so as to give the appearance of a puffed bandage for the hat."

There were no women in his household who could try the contraption out for him, so, thorough in all things, he tried it out for himself to be sure that the instructions were workable.

He bought a little hobby horse for his granddaughter, Anne, and told Martha that Socrates himself would be delighted to ride around on the stick with the little girl. Sometimes Polly sent him a piece of cloth with an airy request that he send her several yards like it and then he would go from one draper to another until the cloth was identified and the yardage sent off.

He could, of course, use his servants for these shopping excursions, but undertaking them himself brought his home nearer to him and that was a great relief to him. He was busy, so busy that at times his head ached for nagging hours and he had to rest in his bed with a cold bandage over his eyes, but he was lonely, too, and he wanted to be with his daughters and in his home and among friends rather than enemies.

When he left for Monticello in January of 1794, he had amassed so much furniture and so many gifts for his daughters that a score of packing cases was needed to contain them and they were forwarded by boat to be off-loaded at Richmond on the James River.

He himself went overland, and arrived in Monticello to a tremendous welcome. Anne was three and talking in whole sentences which delighted Jefferson, who immediately demanded to know of the mother whether she was yet beginning to write. He had a grandson of sixteen months who had been named Thomas Jefferson Randolph.

In the previous spring some mocking birds had nested in the new trees around Monticello and, despite the January weather, he had to go out and look at the nests and warn everybody solemnly not to interfere with the birds whose singing delighted him. Later he tamed a mocking bird which would sit on his shoulder and flutter up the stairs after him. In his youth and as a young man he had been an accomplished violinist, but he had damaged his wrist in a fall in Paris and could play no longer. His tame mocking bird supplied him with music and he did not miss his Mozart and Haydn and Handel so much.

But when he had time to go into the business of his estates, he found they had been badly farmed by paid overseers during his absence, and much of his best land was exhausted from overcropping.

To offset this, new land had been cleared of trees and was ready for cultivation. He owned a total of ten thousand acres, but only two thousand acres could be laid out in crops, the rest being woodland. He had a hundred and fifty-four slaves to feed and care for as well as his own family. The farms around Monticello were not producing enough to take care of his responsibilities.

The corn crop had failed due to a summer drought. The same drought had heavily damaged his fruit trees. Everything needed his personal attention and his bank account was exhausted. He had had to mortgage his lands to pay the expenses at Monticello and also his own expenses in Philadelphia. And when he came home he found that he was so heavily in debt that he could not even borrow fifty dollars which he needed to buy a few sheep to put out to graze on the poorer land of his estates.

But these were the kind of problems that Jefferson liked to tackle. There was a challenge before him— could he wrest enough from the land to feed and clothe all who depended on him, with a surplus left over to pay off his heavy debts? He threw himself into his work with all his energy and though he had arrived from Philadelphia tired, his red hair tinged with grey, the harder he worked at Monticello the younger he seemed to get.

To restore fertility to his lands he decided to rotate the crops. He divided his land into six fields, each in turn to be planted with wheat, corn, potatoes, and peas, rye, clover, and then allowed to lie unproductive for a year. This rotation of crops, as it was called, was just being introduced in England with great success.

Jefferson had read of it in the English papers, and received letters about it from English friends, and he was one of the first American farmers to try the method which worked excellently. He had plenty of animals on his estates: thirty-four horses, eight of them for riding, two hundred and forty-nine head of cattle and three hundred and ninety hogs. These provided fertilizer and he experimented with compost heaps of vegetable matter to provide more fertilizer for his fields. By spring, he had the fifty dollars he needed to buy some sheep. He planted peas in March, and Martha served him the first of the crop six weeks later which delighted him.

"Where else can you get a return like that?" he demanded as the silver dish of steaming fresh peas was put before him on the table. "A bushel of peas planted and we shall have enough to last us the year, either fresh or preserved."

"Don't like peas," said his little granddaughter Anne, destroying a little of his triumph.

"You shall have strawberries in May. I know you'll like them," said Jefferson, "and next year spring lamb of our own raising."

In the months that followed Jefferson spent the greater part of each day on horseback. He breakfasted at dawn, mounted his horse and rode around his estates personally supervising all the work that was being carried on. He returned for a meal at about two in the afternoon, and then received any visitors who dropped in on him. Dinner was served at six in the evening and he went to bed at eight each night.

He loved riding and would ride only the most spirited animals. He rode so well that even Washington, a harsh judge of horseflesh and riders, admired him. His favorite horse was a roan gelding which no one else could ride and it took Jefferson several weeks before he had the gelding gentle. Then he would ride no other. Sometimes he persuaded Martha to let him take little Anne on his saddle, as indeed he had taken Martha when she was a little girl. In dealing with his children and his grandchildren he tried to apply the test of reason to all their requests, but he usually ended up doing what they asked.

There had been no ploughing or preparation of the land at Monticello in the fall of 1793, so there was not much of a harvest in 1794. The pace Jefferson set for himself was more than he could handle at fifty years of age. He was out in all weathers and in September, 1794, suffered such an attack of rheumatism that he had to go to bed for several days. But he was enjoying himself, and what he enjoyed most was the complete retirement from public affairs.

He wrote to Vice President John Adams, "I return to farming with an ardor which I scarcely knew in my youth and which has got the better entirely of my love of study. Instead of writing ten or twelve letters a day, which I have been in the habit of doing as a matter of course, I put off answering my letters now, farmer-like, till a rainy day, and then find them sometimes postponed by other necessary occupations."

He would allow no newspapers in Monticello, for he did not want to be reminded of political problems and he informed Secretary of War Knox that the day might come when he would banish pen and paper and ink from Monticello and never write another line.

And yet, happy though he was, he was pushing himself too hard and his health started to give way under the strain. The attack of rheumatism was followed by a heavy cold and then fever. Jefferson began to think that he had not long to live and worried about what would happen to his family if he died. He wrote to Madison that his health was entirely gone and that his age demanded that he get his affairs in a good condition. He welcomed visitors, begged Madison and others to come and see him, but he warned them not to expect any political talk.

"Be prepared to talk farming," he said. "I don't want to talk of anything else."

Meanwhile, Washington was having trouble with his cabinet. Edmund Randolph was not a satisfactory substitute for Thomas Jefferson as Secretary of State. The British were stirring up trouble with the Indians on the western frontier. Relations with France were deteriorating so that now there was danger of war with France, no longer a Republic but a dictatorship under the control of a man with the curious name of Napoleon Bonaparte.

United States trade down the Mississippi was cut off at New Orleans by Spain. Jefferson, while in office, had sent a mission to Madrid to negotiate for the use of the port of New Orleans for American goods, but nothing had come of it. Washington wondered whether Jefferson, always vitally interested in the western frontier and still dreaming of a nation that extended to the Pacific, would undertake a short mission to Spain to negotiate the New Orleans question. Secretary of State Edmund Randolph wrote asking Jefferson whether he would accept the appointment to Madrid.

"No circumstances, my dear sir, will ever more tempt me to engage in anything public," Jefferson wrote back in reply. And that was the end of that.

Madison tried to coax him back into public office and Edward Rutledge also. But he would not be moved from Monticello.

But in 1796 Washington's second term expired and he announced that he would not serve a third term. A new President had to be elected. John Adams, Vice President and Federalist, was an obvious candidate. Who then would be the Republican candidate? There was only one man of presidential stature on the Republican side in the country, Thomas Jefferson.

His days of retirement at Monticello were coming to a close.

☆ 14 ☆

While Jefferson had been attempting to bring his land, largely neglected for nearly twenty-five years, to the point where its crops would support the one hundred and sixty people who depended on him, the troubles which beset the United States on every side multiplied and grew bigger.

On the western frontier, the Indian tribes unified and raided the settlers and wiped out one army that was sent against them. Another force, dispatched under General "Mad" Anthony Wayne, a great warrior of the Revolutionary War, defeated the massed forces of the Indians at the Battle of Fallen Timbers and secured the Ohio Valley to its juncture with the Mississippi for America. But there were still raids, and pioneer life demanded skill both with the plough and the rifle. The western settlers had to send their produce down the Mississippi for export and New Orleans, as noted, was a foreign town, controlled by Spain. The settlers were still menaced by the Indians and their prosperity was at the mercy of Spain. Their government in Philadelphia could do little to help them.

The Continental Navy had been dissolved at the close of the Revolutionary War and the United States had no warships to guard its merchantmen. Britain, at war with France, claimed the right to search American ships for any goods bound for France. British warships, short of men, boarded American vessels and took off American seamen, declaring that they were British subjects and must serve on the king's ships.

The French then took a page out of Britain's book and seized any American vessels they believed were carrying goods to London or even to the British West Indies. In eight months thirty-two American ships were illegally seized by French vessels. Weakness at sea cost the country dearly, for American merchantmen were also at the mercy of the Barbary pirates who demanded every year a vast sum in gold not to attack American ships.

Meanwhile, a change was beginning to take place among the population of the United States. No sooner had the country become independent than immigrants began to flow in from Europe.

At the time of the Revolution, the greatest number of people in the country were of English ancestry, though there was a heavy and significant sprinkling of Scotch and Irish among them—the Irish none too popular for they were Roman Catholics in a Protestant non-conformist country. Nonetheless three of the men who signed the Declaration of Independence— James Smith, Matthew Thornton and George Taylor —were born in Ireland. And six of Washington's generals were also born in Ireland, including General

Richard Montgomery who had died in a futile but heroic attempt to seize Quebec. These facts have a bearing on what was to occur later.

Now many more Irishmen came and with them, too, Englishmen and other Europeans, drawn to the United States by the hope of a better life with more freedom. And for the first time in the country there began to be some stirrings of dislike for aliens who, it was thought, would bring in foreign ideas and perhaps threaten the freedom of the people.

Among the immigrants was a Swiss named Albert Gallatin. He came of an aristocratic and wealthy family in Switzerland, but gave up his home and his fortune to migrate to America, attracted by the freedom of the country. In his youth he had often met the great French philosopher Voltaire, in exile in Switzerland, and learned from Voltaire to love freedom and hate tyranny. He was a brilliant student both of mathematics and languages and ran away from home to go to America. He landed in Boston, migrated to Maine where he lived for a while in a wilderness cabin, taught French at Harvard and then went to Virginia.

The wealthy Virginians loved learning and loved Gallatin. Patrick Henry, who didn't love learning, and would cheerfully renounce the whole of Latin grammar for a running shot at a deer, met Gallatin and advised him to go west.

"Get out to the frontier," he said. "That's where the true freedom is. There's nothing around here but law books now." He shook his head over Gallatin's learning and grumbled that he would probably become a statesman—a fate that appalled Patrick Henry who had hardly more love of American politicians than he had had of the British politicians who preceded them. He had quarreled with his old friend Thomas Jefferson, and now sneered at Jefferson's fondness for France and French cooking, saying that he had "abjured his native vittles."

Washington also met Gallatin and was so impressed by his learning and industry that he offered him the position of his land agent, but Gallatin refused the offer. He met Thomas Jefferson briefly and agreed with every detail of Jefferson's political philosophy. He had been a Republican before he left Geneva and he remained a Republican the rest of his life.

Gallatin took Patrick Henry's advice and migrated to the Pennsylvania wilderness to speculate in land. He was soon prominent in his community and people began to say that he would be a good man to represent them in Congress.

While all these threats to the country abroad and changes in its population at home had been taking place, Jefferson was farming at Monticello. He took no newspapers. He got his information on public affairs only from visitors and from letters. And then, in the election year of 1796, Madison who had sounded him out several times without success about returning to public life, devised a bold plan. He wanted Jefferson to run for the Presidency in competition with Vice President John Adams.

Adams represented the Federalist viewpoint, which was distrustful of republicanism and leaned towards government by men of property. There was no one to represent the Republican point of view other than Tom Jefferson. Yet Madison knew that if he asked

Jefferson to run for the Presidency, Jefferson would refuse.

Madison decided then to make Jefferson a candidate without obtaining Jefferson's consent. Soon articles were appearing in the Republican newspapers, many of them written by Madison and his friends, suggesting that Thomas Jefferson should run for the Presidency. In a little while the tone of these articles changed to make it plain that Jefferson *was* running for the Presidency, but Madison was careful not to put to Jefferson the question of whether he would run or not. Popular support for Jefferson's candidacy soon made itself felt, particularly in the southern states.

Meanwhile Jefferson continued with his farming, out of touch with the news and discouraging political talk among his visitors. He was not unaware, however, that Madison was pushing him as a presidential candidate, but he made no speech on his own behalf and wrote no letters. He would not even leave Monticello, although John Adams, his opponent, was doing all he could to win votes. Jefferson's major interest was in getting more of his land under cultivation. He worked out a design for a new plough over which he was very excited, and he had at last started a nailery at Monticello to make the nails which he found so expensive to buy. He considered making nails in America as important as winning a title to nobility in Europe. He thought of manufacturing potash for fertilizer but had not enough capital to start such a business. For all his acres of land, he was money-poor and his six-year system of rotating crops would not bring any real results for at least a decade.

But money did not greatly concern him because he

believed it but a token; the real riches of life were to be obtained from the soil. He had to buy wine for his table because his efforts to raise grapes for winemaking were not successful. But he raised his own meat and his own cereals and even got his own fish out of a specially stocked lake. Fruit came from his own trees, and wool for clothing from his own sheep.

While the political world was loud in its arguments about Federalism and Republicanism, France and Britain, banks and paper money, customs, excises and taxes, Jefferson was pondering over the uses to which steam engines could be put in private homes. He thought that using a kitchen fire, a steam engine could be devised to pump water to a cistern on the roof, where it would be available for household use and would be a protection in case of fire.

When visitors remonstrated gently with him over his lack of interest in public affairs, he protested that he was vitally interested in public affairs. "A man who introduces a new plant useful as food into his country is a far greater public benefactor than the most successful of politicians," he said.

"And as for public affairs, if my plough is successful, it would double the acreage which can be ploughed in any season, and thus double the nation's potential food supply. That, I assure you, will be remembered long after the politics of today are forgotten. No, my good sir, the work that is worth doing in the building of our society lies in the fields of agriculture and of science."

And so while Madison and Robert R. Livingston and other Republicans pushed Jefferson's candidacy for the Presidency, Jefferson went on making nails and toying with steam engines and devising a plan for central heating for Monticello which would eliminate dependency on fireplaces. He worked in the fields with his own slaves, getting in the harvest, and he instructed the more intelligent of them in various crafts, so that some were cabinet-makers and others bricklayers and others could operate a wood lathe. To set them free unskilled would be to set them free to starve. So he taught them a trade by which they could earn a living when he gave them their freedom, for he intended to free them. The women folk among them he put to spinning cloth from his own wool for clothing for the others, and while the storm of the presidential election raged over the country, Jefferson was making a little model republic out of Monticello.

Of this tiny republic of ten thousand acres he was already the president, and every citizen of the Republic of Monticello, for such it could be called, had a respected place in society and useful work to do. Jefferson hated to employ men, even slaves, in nonproductive labor. He fitted the house with dumb-waiters, so that food could be brought from the kitchen to the dining room without somebody having to carry it. Besides his nailery he had a blacksmith's shop and a cabinet-maker's shop and a carpenter's shop and a bricklayer's yard. He studied how to make locks and taught some of his Negroes the craft of lockmaking and key cutting, so that everybody at Monticello had a stake in the place.

And yet every now and again, Jefferson would make a statement about national affairs of the country that provided a rallying point for his own supporters. He wrote to Aaron Burr when the country was divided between pro-French and pro-British factions, "We owe gratitude to France, justice to England, good-will to all and subservience to none." In that sentence he summed up what was later to be his own policy in foreign affairs.

The time came at last when Madison felt that he ought to report to Jefferson on the progress of the unauthorized campaign to make him President of the United States. In those days, when there was no organization of political parties such as exists now, the Presidency was awarded the candidate who got the most votes in the Electoral College, the Vice Presidency going to the second highest. Since Adams was a declared candidate for the Presidency and had been actively campaigning for the office, it appeared that he would win, though for a while there was a prospect of a tie in the number of votes won by Adams and Jefferson.

Madison wrote to Jefferson hinting at a tie and Jefferson replied, "There is nothing I so anxiously hope, as that my name may come out either second or third. These would be indifferent to me, as the last would leave me at home the whole year, and the other two-thirds of it."

When the votes were finally counted, Adams had won the election, but by a margin of only three votes—71 to 69. Jefferson wrote to him immediately congratulating him on his election.

"I have never one single moment expected a different issue," he wrote, "and although I know I shall not be believed, yet it is none the less true that I have never wished it."

Madison was concerned that Jefferson might resent

being Vice President to Adams, but Jefferson had no such resentment and wrote to Madison, "I . . . have no feelings which could revolt at a secondary position to Mr. Adams. I am his junior in life, was his junior in Congress, his junior in the diplomatic line, his junior lately in our civil government."

And so Thomas Jefferson set out for Philadelphia on February 20, 1797, to take up public life again, not as Secretary of State, but as Vice President in the administration of John Adams.

☆ 15 ☆

Thomas Jefferson's term as Vice President of the United States was spent in achieving a great deal by doing very little. Nobody then was quite sure of just how much power the Vice President had. It was laid down that he should preside over the Senate and of course he would take over the Presidency in case of the death of the President. But presiding over the Senate was hardly a full-time occupation for a man of the calibre of Thomas Jefferson. And roly-poly President Adams, who was called "Mr. Rotundity," because of his little round head and pudgy figure, was in excellent health. When he went to Philadelphia as Vice President Jefferson believed he would not have very much to do and would be able to spend a considerable amount of his time at Monticello.

Perhaps he might have been able to do so but for the mounting speed of the crises into which the country was headed. Relations with France had so deteriorated that there was a fever through the country for war with France to protect American shipping.

The Federalist Party was in power and its policy was anti-French. Jefferson watched while a public furor against the French, and by extension all foreigners, gripped the nation.

Alexander Hamilton had retired as Secretary of the Treasury in January of 1795. He was now practicing law in New York. But while he had retired from the Cabinet he had not retired from politics. Behind the scenes, Hamilton was fighting to gain control of the Federal party from Adams. And very soon Jefferson discovered that Hamilton, from his New York law office, was actually running the Cabinet and the government.

The Secretary of State was Thomas Pickering—a cold, stern, puritanical man who had, through his brother's influence, become Postmaster General under Washington. That position brought him into contact with Alexander Hamilton. Hamilton before his retirement won him over and rewarded him with promotions finally transferring him from the Post Office to the State Department. Thomas Pickering was John Adams' Secretary of State but he was Alexander Hamilton's man.

The Secretary of the Treasury was Oliver Wolcott who had been appointed auditor of the Treasury Department by Hamilton. Soon Hamilton had promoted him to Comptroller of the Treasury. When Hamilton retired Washington appointed Wolcott Secretary of the Treasury in his stead and John Adams let him remain in the post. And as with Pickering, Wolcott may have been Adams' Secretary of the Treasury but he was Hamilton's man.

Secretary of War, James McHenry, an immigrant

from Ireland also owed his position to Hamilton's influence, or thought he did, and, too, was a Hamilton man. He owed nothing whatever to John Adams. The fourth member of the Cabinet, the Attorney General, had little influence on national affairs.

The Cabinet in his hands, Hamilton also had a strong following in the Congress; so, from his New York law office, unknown to John Adams, he manipulated the government of the United States to give effect to his policies rather than those of Adams.

Hamilton had, of course, opposition. His great opponent in the Congress was the young Swiss immigrant, Albert Gallatin. Gallatin had been elected to the Congress from Pennsylvania and proved himself such a master of finance that in his first term he was challenging, blocking, and even defeating many of the financial measures that Hamilton wished the Congress to pass.

President John Adams in his message to Congress reviewed the threat of war with France, announced plans for a new attempt at negotiations and meanwhile urged that the country arm itself. A stormy debate broke out in the Congress immediately on framing the reply to the President's address.

The Federalists, who were for war, were for denouncing the message as too conciliatory to France. The Democratic-Republicans, who were for peace, thought the language of the President's message gave unnecessary offense to France. The debate raged for several days and members were not above flinging insults at each other.

Gallatin was critized on the grounds of his foreign accent and birth and another member criticized Matthew Lyon, a Vermont republican, for his humble origin. He was an Irish immigrant. Lyon replied that he rejoiced that he was not descended from "Puritans who punish their horses for breaking the sabbath or from those who persecuted the Quakers and burned the witches."

Eventually Lyon and Roger Grissold, a Federalist, got into a fight on the floor of the Congress. Grissold beat Lyon on the head with a hickory stick and Lyon defended himself by snatching up the coal tongs. The two clinched and rolled on the floor of the House and were finally separated by their colleagues.

War fever was coupled, as noted, with distrust of foreigners and it certainly seemed significant to the Federalists that many who supported Jefferson were of recent foreign extraction. When Adams' mission to France, aimed at ridding American ships of search and seizure by French shipping, failed, he turned to his Cabinet for advice on the next step to take.

His Cabinet made contact with Hamilton and gave the President Hamilton's recommendations. Hamilton did not propose a declaration of war on France, but a preparation for immediate war. Merchant vessels should be sent to sea armed, a standing army of sixteen thousand men should be recruited, a Navy should be built, the old French treaty should be broken, and the tax system should be put on a war basis.

There should not be an alliance with England but perhaps Britain might agree to convoy American shipping. Adams recommended such measures to the House, not knowing that he was putting Hamilton's policies into effect. The House voted the necessary legislation and overnight the country was in a state of undeclared war with France.

Now all refugees and exiles became suspect. Attempts in Ireland to overthrow British rule had failed again and many Irish refugees came to the United States to find themselves not heroes but villains for lifting a hand against Britain. Many Frenchmen came also and soon stories were being put about in the Federalist press that Irishmen and French Jacobins were arming to overthrow the United States. One Federalist Senator announced that Pennsylvania was "full of United Irishmen in camps, Free Masons and the most God-provoking Democrats this side of Hell." Few stopped to consider the unlikelihood of an alliance between Irish Roman Catholics and French Free Masons.

Jefferson, of course, was to blame for this foreign menace and bands took to playing "The Rogues March" outside his house in Philadelphia. He appeared unperturbed, never went out into society and dined only with friends from the Philosophical Society, with whom he could discuss such fascinating news as the discovery in Greenbriar County of the bones of a lion-like creature whose claws were eight inches long. The creature was given the name of *Megalonyx Jeffersoni* and Jefferson wondered whether any specimens were still living in the unexplored American west. He also found that a young surveyor was going into the plains beyond the Mississippi, where the Indians reported there were herds of wild horses. He begged the young man to make extensive notes on the wild horse herds for such herds he believed would soon be extinct.

Thomas Jefferson's seeming unconcern over the rush to war and the hostility to foreigners that was sweeping the country was calculated. He was putting a theory of his own to the test. The theory was that the people themselves, once they were possessed of the facts, would undo any harm being done. Let the Federalists have their day. Let them have their friendship with England and their war against France. Let them persecute unfortunate aliens. Eventually the country would awaken to the terrible injustices that were being done and wipe the Federalists out. That would be the end of the Federalist Party with its distrust of the mass of society and its leaning towards an aristocratic form of government.

Two acts were now rushed through the Congress against the advice of the wiser of the Federalists. The Alien Act authorized the President to expel, without hearing or trial, any alien he judged "dangerous to the peace and safety of the United States," or had "reasonable grounds to suspect is concerned in any treasonable or secret machinations against the government."

Under the act, any alien could be deported on suspicion alone! The Sedition Act provided for a fine of up to two thousand dollars and imprisonment of not more than two years for the writing, printing, uttering, or publishing of "any false, scandalous, and malicious writing or writings against the government of the United States . . . with intent to defame . . . the good people of the United States or to stir up sedition within the United States, or to excite any unlawful combinations therein."

The Sedition Act in effect abolished the Bill of

Rights and Jefferson was horrified to see it pass the Congress. When it came before the Senate, Jefferson presided over the debate without interfering on one side or the other. He did not believe the country would tolerate the act if it became law and the passage of the act seemed to him the first step in the suicide of the Federalist Party. Hamilton himself opposed these two acts.

"Let us not establish a tyranny," he pleaded. "Energy is a very different thing from violence." But the country in its hysteria would not listen to Hamilton. Jefferson's comment was, "I consider these laws as merely an experiment on the American mind to see how far it will bear an avowed violation of the Constitution." In short, Jefferson wanted to see just how republican were the citizens of the republic of the United States of America.

He believed that for a while a Federalist reign of terror would engulf the United States as a republican reign of terror had engulfed France.

It was not hard to predict who would be the first victim of the Sedition Act. He was none other than Matthew Lyon, the outspoken ex-officer in Washington's Army who was a strong supporter of Thomas Jefferson and had been in a fight with Grissold on the floor of the Congress. Lyon, a Congressman from Vermont at the time, was charged with intent "to stir up sedition, and to bring the President and government . . . into contempt."

All that Lyon had actually done was criticize President Adams whom he said he could not support because he was surrounded by people who put aside the public welfare in their grasp for power. He also criticized Adams for "ridiculous pomp, foolish adulation, and selfish avarice."

Lyon was not a man to moderate his tongue but nothing he said could be reasonably interpreted as treasonable. Nonetheless he was brought before a justice of the Supreme Court, tried, and found guilty under the Sedition Act. During his trial Lyon would not back down in the slightest from his criticism of the President and the government. He declared that the Sedition Act was unconstitutional and that everything he had said was true. He even asked the judge point blank whether he had not often dined at the President's table and observed his "ridiculous pomp and parade." The judge said he hadn't. The jury convicted Lyon, sentenced him to four months in prison and a fine of one thousand dollars.

The conviction shocked the whole nation except the most ardent of the Federalists. "A curious sport," quipped little Jimmy Madison visiting Jefferson in Philadelphia. "The Romans are devouring the Lyons and claiming all is done on behalf of the Christians."

"I suppose," said Jefferson, "that there is a kind of genius of stupidity as well as a genius of intelligence. The arrest and conviction of Lyon in that case is a masterpiece of blundering. I can think of nothing these extremists could do which would injure their cause more."

"Do you propose to speak out against these measures?" asked Madison.

"The measures will speak out against themselves," replied Jefferson. "No words of mine will have half their eloquence. When I was a young man, practicing law, I defended a slave who was a slave only because of a social offense by his great grandmother. I was horrified when the man who instructed me in law, George Wythe, appeared against me and secured from the court a verdict that kept my client in slavery for the misdeeds of his great grandmother. I remonstrated with Mr. Wythe for taking such a case. He replied that it was not the function of a lawyer to change laws. A lawyer best served the public by demonstrating the effect of laws.

"I believe that that case had a great influence on mitigating the laws governing slaves in Virginia. No, Mr. Madison, all we have to do is sit quiet while the Federalists first build a coffin for their party and then close the lid on it."

Shocking as was the conviction of Lyon, what followed was just as bad. A little while later Anthony Hazwell printed an advertisement in his newspaper, the *Vermont Gazette*. The advertisement was paid for by Lyon and publicized a lottery to raise money to pay his fine.

It stated that Lyon was "holden by the oppressive hand of usurpt power in a loathsome prison, deprived almost of the right of reason and suffering all the indignities which can be heaped on him by a hard-hearted savage who has, to the disgrace of Federalism, been elevated to a station where he can satiate his barbarity on the misery of his victim."

The wording was Lyon's and the rigors of jail obviously hadn't curbed his tongue. The same judge who had convicted Lyon convicted Hazwell. Hazwell produced evidence to prove that Lyon was being brutally treated in jail. This did not impress the judge or the jury. Hazwell was fined two hundred dollars and sentenced to two months confinement. He was the father of seventeen children and he was born in England.

The first two victims of the Sedition Act then were both foreign born. "We witness some strange matters indeed," said Jefferson. "England comes to the defense of Ireland and both are jailed in America."

The next major victim of the Act was also English-born. He was Thomas Cooper, who edited a pro-Jefferson paper and was both an educator and a scientist. He was a friend also of Jefferson's, and he criticized President Adams for saddling the people with a permanent Navy, borrowing money at eight percent when lower rates were to be had, and for public expressions, which, Cooper felt, had aggravated the position with France.

Cooper was hustled into court where he undertook to defend himself but his defense was of no avail. The judge, Justice Samuel Chase, was so partial as to attack Cooper's statements without evidence to support the attack, and Cooper was sent to prison for six months and fined two hundred dollars.

It was Scotland's turn next. In Richmond, Virginia, James Thomson Callendar, a Scottish-born writer was indicted for criticizing the President. Three of Virginia's greatest lawyers, all friends of Jefferson's, volunteered to defend him. They were Thomas Nicholas, William Wirt, and George Hay. They appeared before the same Justice Chase who had imprisoned Cooper. He cut the lawyers off during their addresses, ordered them about, and bullied them into frustration. Callendar was sentenced to nine months in jail and fined two hundred dollars.

Jefferson's friends were now thoroughly alarmed and asked him to intervene, or at least publicly head the growing opposition to the Alien and Sedition Acts. Publicly Jefferson would do nothing. From his viewpoint it was essential that the nation itself awake to the injustice of the two acts and demand an end to the persecutions under them.

"Wisdom and justice in ruling must not rest only in the hands of a few leaders," he told his friends. "Wisdom and justice in public affairs must spring from the mass of our people if our republic is to survive."

Many years later a wise judge put the matter in a different way. "People," he said, "get the kind of government they deserve."

Privately, however, Jefferson helped to organize a fund-raising campaign to free Matthew Lyon. The campaign was so popular that a thousand dollars in gold and a similar amount in silver was raised. Lyon, his fine paid, was set free and departed immediately for Philadelphia to take his seat in the Congress to which he had been re-elected. He was given a hero's welcome in every town he went through, and at times a procession several miles long followed his sleigh for he was freed in mid-winter.

Jefferson had been carefully devising a plan to rid the country of the oppressive legislation. When Congress adjourned in 1798, he returned to Monticello and had a meeting there of his friends, including W. C. Nicholas of Virginia and John Breckenridge. They talked about the Alien and Sedition Acts and Jefferson made a few points concerning the powers of the Federal government.

"There are three points concerning the Federal government which should be borne in mind," he said. "The first is that the Federal government was created by the individual states. The second is that the Federal government is the agent of the states which created it. The third which follows from these two is that the states have perfect authority to criticize the actions of the Federal government and they may also void the actions of the Federal government they hold unconstitutional."

"Surely," cried Nicholas, "you are not advocating a doctrine which would make the states superior to the Federal government?"

"We are not concerned here with a matter of sovereignty but with the deeper matter of liberty," said Jefferson. "Liberty is still guaranteed in our Constitution and particularly in our Bill of Rights. If the Federal government falls into the error of denying the Bill of Rights by passing legislation like the Alien and Sedition Acts, the state governments are not obliged to fall into the same error. Rather it is their duty to point to the error and demand by resolutions in their own legislatures that the error be abolished.

"We will have fallen on sad times when we entrust our liberty to a vast central agency and neglect to keep a guard on it ourselves. Neglect of liberty is the first step towards loss of liberty."

The result of this conference was that, with Jefferson's aid, a resolution was drawn up, in effect asserting the right of the states to nullify unconstitutional actions of the Federal government. It was presented by Breckenridge to the Kentucky Legislature and adopted with enthusiasm. The Kentucky resolution contained a threat of secession if the Federal government continued to act in a manner judged tyrannical.

A similar resolution, though somewhat watered down, was passed in the Virginia Legislature. The doctrine of State's Rights had been proclaimed by Thomas Jefferson. He could not foresee that, by an unwarranted extension, it would eventually lead to the Civil War.

☆ 16 ☆

While the Federalists gleefully pushed their persecutions under the Alien and Sedition Acts in an attempt
to stifle all Republican opposition the country went to
war with France. The war was undeclared and waged
only at sea. A United States squadron under Commo-
dore John Barry went to the West Indies to protect
American shipping and the French frigate *Insurgente*
was forced to strike her colors after a brief action with
the new United States frigate *Constellation*.

On land there was tremendous mobilization. George
Washington was called out of retirement to head a
greatly expanded United States Army. Using Secretary of War McHenry as his agent, Hamilton got himself appointed second in command. Madison had told
Jefferson many years before that Hamilton was ambitious to be a great military commander. When Jefferson
heard of Hamilton's appointment, he recalled how on
one occasion Hamilton had looked at three portraits
displayed on the walls of Jefferson's office.

"Whose pictures are these?" Hamilton had asked.

"They are the portraits of the world's greatest men," said Jefferson. "Bacon, Newton, and Locke."

Hamilton paused for some time and said, "The greatest man that ever lived was Julius Caesar."

"Perhaps," suggested Madison slyly, hearing of this anecdote, "Mr. Hamilton is intent on out-Caesaring Julius."

This big mobilization both of the Navy and the Army cost money. President Adams, still innocent of the fact that his Cabinet was largely controlled by Hamilton, found himself faced with the need of borrowing huge sums on the public credit to pay for the Army and Navy. But when he turned to the Federalist financiers, who had money to loan, they would offer it only at eight percent interest despite the belief that the nation was on the verge of an all out war with France.

Money borrowed meant taxes to make repayment and the taxes fell heaviest on the Republicans—small property owners who could ill afford to pay. Adams' popularity began to wane and when after some months no French invasion materialized (the Federalist press had been confidently predicting one), he found himself blamed for the tax burden and indeed for the whole war hysteria. Added to that, he was blamed also for the persecutions under the Alien and Sedition Acts. Without publicly moving a finger, Jefferson had allowed the Federalist Party to destroy itself.

Many wealthy Americans, not rabid Federalists, wondered just how vexed the situation between the United States and France really was. No one could deny that French ships had seized American merchantmen, but some began to feel that perhaps these grievances could be negotiated. Secret commissioners sent to France by Adams had not only been rebuffed but been told that America must pay money for France's good-will.

The report these commissioners brought back when published greatly damaged Jefferson's position as a friend of France and aggravated the demand for war. Still some felt that a diplomatic approach might be possible. One day Dr. James Logan, an old friend of Jefferson's, called on him in Philadelphia.

"I am going on a private mission of my own to France," he said. "Could you give me letters to some of your friends in Paris?"

"By all means," said Jefferson. "I presume you are indeed travelling as a private individual?"

"I am indeed," said Dr. Logan, "but I am also travelling as an American."

"It is possible," said Jefferson, "that as a private individual and an American you may be able to learn more about the French attitude towards ourselves than did our late commissioners."

"That is precisely what I have in mind, sir," said Dr. Logan.

He went and returned with the report that the French government—no longer a republic—was anxious for peace. Others undertook similar missions and were not long in telling President Adams that France by no means desired war with the United States.

Then came a letter to President Adams from the French minister of Foreign Affairs saying that the French government would receive with every respect any minister sent to negotiate the differences which existed with the United States. Adams informed the Congress, the war hysteria died away, and a commissioner was sent to France to negotiate a peace, but the damage to the Federalist Party had been done, and ahead loomed the election of a new President.

President Adams, so long deceived about his Cabinet ministers, tried to put his house in order. He was a self-important little man, but nonetheless a man of great character. He had had the courage to defend the British soldiers on trial for the Boston massacre in the days before the Revolution. When he did that, he risked his whole profession as a lawyer practicing in Boston.

He had been the Samson of New England in bringing about the independence of the nation, and Jefferson, who differed with him politically, nonetheless admired him tremendously. Adams now asked Secretary of War McHenry for his resignation. McHenry resigned and Samuel Dexter was appointed in his stead.

He asked for the resignation of his Secretary of State, but Pickering refused to resign. Adams discharged him and replaced him with John Marshall. These Cabinet shake-ups came too late, however, to help President Adams in the coming election.

The names of two men were soon before the public for the Presidency—Aaron Burr and Thomas Jefferson. Both were Republicans: Burr enormously popular in the northern states where he had made out of the Tammany society a political machine that was to influence American politics for the next two hundred years, and Jefferson, popular all over the country as the champion of the little man.

The election campaign that followed was one of the most vicious ever conducted in the whole history of the country to date. The Federalists were hopelessly split between supporters of Adams and supporters of Hamilton. They united only in denouncing Jefferson. He was condemned as an atheist, as an anarchist, and as a man who, if elected, would plunge the country into the kind of bloody revolution which had deluged France.

Many years before, Jefferson had attacked the Church of England which, as the established church, was supported by public taxes. Separation of church and state was essential to freedom in Jefferson's mind. He also earnestly believed that men should be completely free to worship according to the dictates of their own conscience and not compelled, as was once the case, to attend a particular church.

Now some of the churchmen struck back at him. Some of Jefferson's sayings were quoted unfairly or out of context to prove he was an infidel.

Jefferson had once written advocating religious tolerance, "It does me no injury for my neighbor to say there are twenty gods or no god. It neither picks my pocket nor breaks my leg." William Linn, a minister of the Dutch Reformed Church, quoted this saying in a pamphlet designed to prove Jefferson an atheist.

Others of the clergy took up the attack. The Reverend Cotton Mather Smith of Massachusetts accused Jefferson of accumulating his property by robbing a widow and fatherless children while acting as executor of their estate, while another said that Jefferson on passing a dilapidated church had sneered, "It is good enough for Him who was born in a manger."

To all such accusations and slanders Jefferson remained silent. But if Jefferson was silent, his friends were not and he had many of them. There was first of all James Madison, then Senator James Monroe of Virginia, and then Congressman Robert R. Livingston of New York, and Congressmen Albert Gallatin and Thomas McKean of Pennsylvania. And besides these, hundreds of thousands of Americans whose names Jefferson never knew but who knew that Tom Jefferson alone would defend their rights.

While the campaign raged about the nation with scurrilous attacks on Jefferson in the press being answered by Jefferson's friends, he himself did nothing. He returned to Monticello, took up again the management of his estates and enjoyed having his family around him.

The family was growing. He had two grandchildren and now Polly had married a boyhood friend, John Wayles Eppes, who was her cousin. Jefferson, unable to refrain from giving Polly a few words of advice on marriage, told her, "Harmony is the first object to be aimed at. Nothing can preserve affection but a determination in husband and wife to consider the love of the other as of more value than any other object whatever. If the advice I give you is the means of saving you from a single heartache it will have contributed a great deal to my happiness."

He brought back to Monticello not voluminous papers to be studied but toys for his grandchildren. The summer went happily. He left Monticello only once to pay a visit to some friends in nearby Bedford. Madison visited him and Jefferson refused to say a word about politics. They rode together around the

Monticello estate and talked about gardening and the weather.

By July, Jefferson had finished getting in the harvest and on July the Fourth of 1800, the twenty-fourth anniversary of the Declaration of Independence, Jefferson was trying out a new Forte Piano (as a pianoforte was then called) and had decided that it was a much better instrument than his harpsichord. It had had a rough journey to Monticello and while the country was concerned about whether he or Aaron Burr would be the next President, Jefferson was tuning his new instrument.

That wonderful summer which gave Thomas Jefferson the heaviest wheat crop he had been able to harvest at Monticello also brought him a tremendous harvest of votes. He made no speeches and went on no tours but when at last all the votes were counted the result was a tie. Seventy-three votes for Jefferson and seventy-three for Burr. Adams had gained only sixty-five.

When Adams heard the result of the voting, he said, "I understand you are to beat me in this contest and I will only say that I will be as faithful a subject as any you will have." To Jefferson it seemed that Adams was taking the matter personally. For him the election was not a matter of individuals but of individual principles.

"Mr. Adams," he said, "there is no personal contest between you and me. Two systems of principles on the subject of government divide our fellow citizens into two parties. Were we both to die today, tomorrow there would be two other names in place of ours."

"I believe you are right," said Adams. "We are but

passive instruments and should not suffer this matter to affect our personal dispositions."

But Adams was hurt and a little bitter.

With a tie in the Electoral College between Jefferson and Burr, the matter of who should be President was put to a vote of the House of Representatives.

The balloting started on the eleventh of February, 1801, in a raging snowstorm and in the new city of Washington, D. C. Ballot followed ballot without the tie being broken.

One Congressman, Joseph H. Nicholson of Maryland, though desperately ill, was carried in a litter through the snow to the capitol to vote. He remained all day and as each ballot was taken scribbled Jefferson's name on the slip given him.

The first day brought no decision. The second day brought no decision. The balloting continued for a week still with deadlock. Jefferson living, in a boarding house, wrote to Polly saying how much he missed her and Martha. "I feel a sincere wish indeed to see our government brought back to its Republican principles, to see that kind of government firmly fixed to which my whole life has been devoted. I hope we shall now see it so established as that when I retire it may be under full security that we are to continue free and happy."

Tremendous pressure was now put on Jefferson to promise a few political favors in return for enough votes to give him the Presidency. Adams came to him and said, "You have only to say you will do justice to the public creditors, maintain the Navy, and not disturb those holding office and the government will instantly be put into your hands."

Jefferson said, scarcely raising his voice, "I will not come into the government by capitulation."

There were some thirty members of the Congress staying at the boarding house where Jefferson was living, and although Jefferson was Vice President and likely to be President, he sat anywhere at the dining table there was room for him. Somebody suggested that he should be seated at the head of the table but one of the Republican Congressmen replied, "Mr. Jefferson must not be allowed to forget that he is one of the people and that all are equal."

The reply made in Jefferson's hearing made him smile. It was exactly what he felt himself.

It was not until February 7th, 1801, that the deadlock in the House was broken. Thirty-six ballots had been taken before enough votes were given Jefferson to elect him President of the United States of America.

When the news was brought to him he was standing by a window of one of the public rooms at the boarding house. He made no immediate comment but looked out the window to see that the snow had stopped falling and the landscape was glittering under the sunshine.

"The gales of spring are over," he said at last.

"I beg your pardon," said the messenger.

"You would not understand, my friend, but Mr. Madison would."

There would be now, he thought, a republican summer for the whole nation.

END OF THE THIRD VOLUME

AUTHOR'S NOTE

The public libraries of the nation have a good supply of excellent books about Jefferson of which perhaps half consist of Jefferson's own writings edited by one person or another. I am not therefore going to try to provide the reader with a bibliography, but will only mention the books which I found particularly helpful in writing my present volume about Thomas Jefferson.

Two very good books are now available in paperback. They are *Thomas Jefferson,* by Professor Stuart Gerry Brown of Syracuse University and *Jefferson* by Saul K. Padover. Both are indexed and the latter is abridged. These are both informed, lively and intelligent books about Jefferson and very readable. For me they read as well as a good novel, which cannot be said of many Jefferson biographies which are tedious and at times shrill in their defense of Jefferson as opposed to Hamilton. I will say a little more about that further on.

For readers who want to get just a general view of Jefferson, I would recommend *Thomas Jefferson and His World,* a product of American Heritage Junior Library. This is a remarkably good piece of work with plenty of pictures and anecdotes to liven the way from cover to cover.

The best view of Jefferson at home, I think, is provided in *The Domestic Life of Thomas Jefferson,* by Sarah N. Randolph, his great-granddaughter. I am not sure whether this book is still in print. The edition I used was published in 1871 by Harper and Brothers and I borrowed it from the University of Southern California Library. That University was extremely helpful in letting me use all their library facilities for my own research, and I am much indebted to it for this service. The book itself is a delight, consisting of the greater bulk of Jefferson's correspondence with his daughters and friends, to whom he wrote quite openly about his feelings and problems.

Another useful book of Jefferson's writing is *Jefferson Himself,* edited by Bernard Mayo; and *Jefferson and Hamilton* by Claude G. Bowers gives a very detailed account of the differences which developed early between these two great men. Bowers' book also has the virtue of setting things in their perspective and is really a first-class study of the whole political situation during the presidencies of Washington and Adams. It is good reading, being both instructive and amusing.

My present volume deals with the most tumultuous years of Jefferson's life, when he came into conflict with Hamilton at almost every turn of the political road. There is a deplorable tendency among many writers concerned with this period to make Jefferson the *hero* and Hamilton the *villain*, and I have tried to avoid that. It must be borne in mind that although there was a one hundred and eighty degree difference in their views on many subjects, both were patriots. Hamilton would do nothing that he did not consider to be for the benefit of his country, and neither would Jefferson. Indeed, it was the very intensity of their patriotism, I believe, that sharpened the conflict between them, for each was convinced that the other's policies would, if pursued, ruin the country they loved.

In any event, history shows that both were very wrong on important points. Jefferson was quite wrong in opposing Hamilton's financial policies. Without some such plan as the national bank, it is difficult to see how the nation's business could have been carried on and expanded in the infancy of the Republic. Hamilton was equally wrong in believing that Jefferson's determination to leave as much of the government as possible in the hands of the people would lead to anarchy. Hamilton believed in government by men of property; Jefferson believed in government by men, period. In defense of Hamilton it has to be pointed out that Jefferson's concept of a complete republic had never been tried. The nearest approach to such a government was in Great Britain, but the government there at the time was actually an aristocracy, for the power of veto lay with the hereditary House of Lords, and indeed remained in the House of Lords until the present century when it was removed following an impasse over the Irish question.

So Hamilton had history on his side, but Jefferson had something more powerful than history. He had the future. And with that weapon he won.

I have to say a word about democracy and republic. These days there is a tendency to differentiate between the two, and some people are fond of pointing out that the United States was conceived as a republic and not a democracy, as if a republic was something to be lauded and a democracy a snare and a delusion. Actually the two words are but the Latin and Greek terms for the same thing. Republic, which is a Latin derivative, means a state in which the government is carried on by the people or their elected representatives. Democracy, a Greek derivative, means government by the people or their representatives. Both definitions are taken from the Oxford dictionary. We haven't got an Anglo-Saxon word for this condition. The nearest we can come to it is commonwealth.

Whatever the confusions in the modern mind (as the result of the neglect of classical studies) they did not exist in Jefferson's time, and his party became known for a time as the Democratic-Republican party. This party was not the modern Republican Party, which did not come into being until several decades after Jefferson's death.

I have necessarily had to telescope a great deal of material in this book out of mercy for the reader. My object has not been to draw every twig on the tree, but to sketch the trunk and the main branches. If, carrying this figure a little further, the thing comes out looking like a tree, I shall be quite happy.

LEONARD WIBBERLEY

Hermosa Beach
California

INDEX

Harrison, Benjamin, 8
Hazwell, Anthony, 158-159
Henry, Patrick, 8-9, 32, 143-144

Jacobins, 90-95
Jefferson, Martha ("Patsy"),
4, 6, 7-8, 41-42, 48, 61-62,
67, 85, 134, 137, 138, 170
Jefferson, Mary ("Polly"), 4,
42-45, 48, 61-62, 64, 134,
168, 170

Knox, John, 16, 119, 121-122,
139

Lafayette, Marquis de, 18,
86, 87-90, 92
Lee, Richard Bland, 31-33
Little Sarah, The, 106-108,
111-116
Livingston, Robert R., 146,
168
Louis XVI of France, 21, 89-90, 93-95, 97-98, 122, 130
Lyon, Matthew, 153, 156-158, 160

Madison, James, 8-14, 22, 26-27, 31, 33, 36, 46-47, 51,
54-55, 57, 62-71, 74-75,
79, 81-83, 94, 104, 117,
139-140, 144-146, 148-149, 157-158, 163-164,
168, 171
Marie Antoinette, 89, 100,
130

Marshall, John, 166
McHenry, James, 151, 163,
166
Monroe, James, 8, 168

National Gazette, 71-72, 114
Nicholas, W. C., 160-161

Pickering, Thomas, 151, 166

Randolph, Anne, 134, 135,
137, 138
Randolph, Edmund, 128,
139-140
Randolph, John, 16, 32
Randolph, Thomas Jefferson,
135
Randolph, Thomas Mann, 7-8, 41

Smith, Cotton Mather, 167

Treaty of Alliance, 97-99, 101

Washington, George, 5-6, 12,
15-16, 20-21, 23, 28, 30,
36-38, 46-47, 52, 54-55,
74-79, 87, 88, 97, 98-102,
105-108, 111-112, 113-115,
116, 118-123, 124-132,
134, 138, 139-140, 144,
163
White, Alexander, 31, 33
Whitney, Eli, 49
Wolcott, Oliver, 151
Wythe, George, 158

★ 180 ★